Exploring

Science
How Science Works

9

Series Editor:
Mark Levesley

Penny Johnson
Steve Gray
Sue Kearsey

PEARSON

Longman

Edinburgh Gate
Harlow, Essex

This book also includes Active Book

Contents

How to use this book

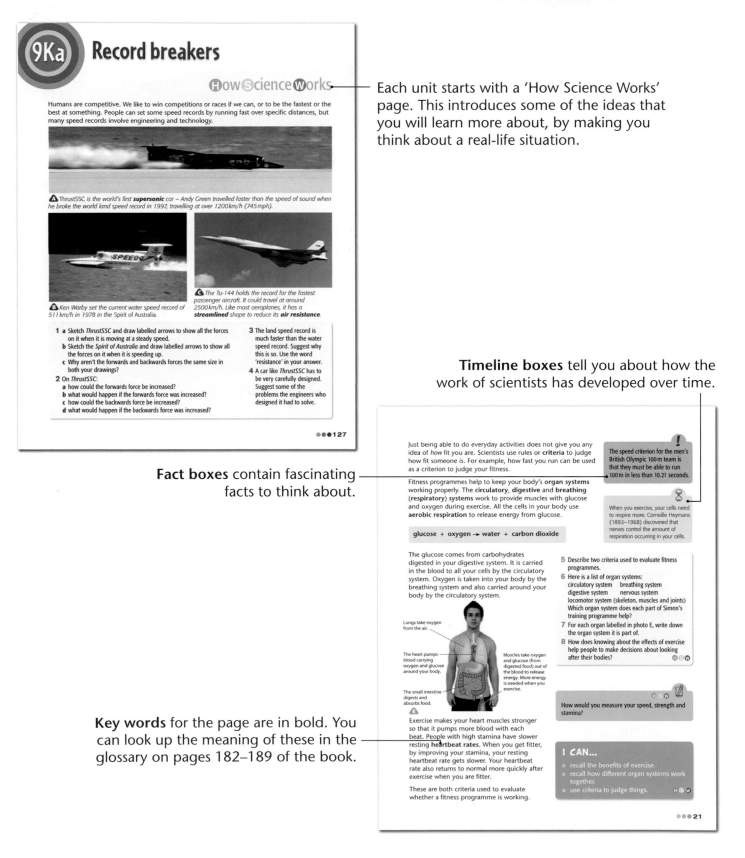

Each unit starts with a 'How Science Works' page. This introduces some of the ideas that you will learn more about, by making you think about a real-life situation.

Timeline boxes tell you about how the work of scientists has developed over time.

Fact boxes contain fascinating facts to think about.

Key words for the page are in bold. You can look up the meaning of these in the glossary on pages 182–189 of the book.

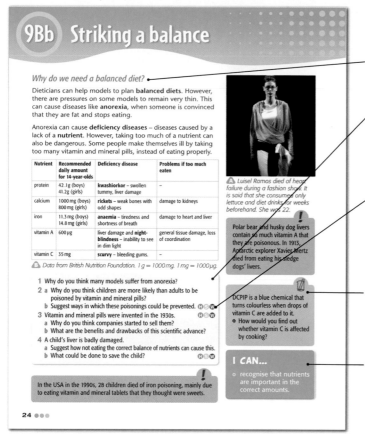

9Bb Striking a balance

Why do we need a balanced diet?

Dieticians can help models to plan **balanced diets**. However, there are pressures on some models to remain very thin. This can cause diseases like **anorexia**, when someone is convinced that they are fat and stops eating.

Anorexia can cause **deficiency diseases** – diseases caused by a lack of a **nutrient**. However, taking too much of a nutrient can also be dangerous. Some people make themselves ill by taking too many vitamin and mineral pills, instead of eating properly.

Nutrient	Recommended daily amount for 14-year-olds	Deficiency disease	Problems if too much eaten
protein	42.1g (boys) 41.2g (girls)	**kwashiorkor** – swollen tummy, liver damage	–
calcium	1000 mg (boys) 800 mg (girls)	**rickets** – weak bones with odd shapes	damage to kidneys
iron	11.3 mg (boys) 14.8 mg (girls)	**anaemia** – tiredness and shortness of breath	damage to heart and liver
vitamin A	600 µg	liver damage and **night-blindness** – inability to see in dim light	general tissue damage, loss of coordination
vitamin C	35 mg	**scurvy** – bleeding gums.	–

⚠ *Data from British Nutrition Foundation. 1 g = 1000 mg. 1 mg = 1000µg.*

1 Why do you think many models suffer from anorexia?
2 a Why do you think children are more likely than adults to be poisoned by vitamin and mineral pills?
  b Suggest ways in which these poisonings could be prevented. Ⓗ Ⓢ Ⓦ
3 Vitamin and mineral pills were invented in the 1930s. Ⓗ Ⓢ Ⓦ
  a Why do you think companies started to sell them?
  b What are the benefits and drawbacks of this scientific advance?
4 A child's liver is badly damaged.
  a Suggest how not eating the correct balance of nutrients can cause this.
  b What could be done to save the child? Ⓗ Ⓢ Ⓦ

! In the USA in the 1990s, 28 children died of iron poisoning, mainly due to eating vitamin and mineral tablets that they thought were sweets.

⚠ *Luisel Ramos died of heart failure during a fashion show. It is said that she consumed only lettuce and diet drinks for weeks beforehand. She was 22.*

Polar bear and husky dog livers contain so much vitamin A that they are poisonous. In 1913, Antarctic explorer Xavier Mertz died from eating his sledge dogs' livers.

🔍 DCPIP is a blue chemical that turns colourless when drops of vitamin C are added to it.
● How would you find out whether vitamin C is affected by cooking?

I CAN...
● recognise that nutrients are important in the correct amounts.

24 ●●●

You should be able to answer this question by the time you have finished the page.

Questions are spread throughout the page so you can answer them as you go through the topic.

Where you see this 'How Science Works' icon, it means that the question or piece of text is about practical or enquiry skills, how science has changed over time, or how science is used and applied in real life.

Practical boxes give you ideas for investigations and practical work. Sometimes there is a picture to give you ideas for planning your investigation.

I can... boxes help you to assess what you've learned and check your progress.

Each unit ends with a 'How Science Works' page. Here you can apply what you've learned to a real-life situation.

These give you extra information about the topic.

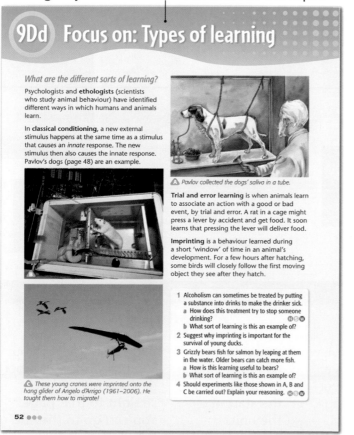

9Dd Focus on: Types of learning

What are the different sorts of learning?

Psychologists and **ethologists** (scientists who study animal behaviour) have identified different ways in which humans and animals learn.

In **classical conditioning**, a new external stimulus happens at the same time as a stimulus that causes an *innate* response. The new stimulus then also causes the innate response. Pavlov's dogs (page 48) are an example.

⚠ *Pavlov collected the dogs' saliva in a tube.*

Trial and error learning is when animals learn to associate an action with a good or bad event, by trial and error. A rat in a cage might press a lever by accident and get food. It soon learns that pressing the lever will deliver food.

Imprinting is a behaviour learned during a short 'window' of time in an animal's development. For a few hours after hatching, some birds will closely follow the first moving object they see after they hatch.

1 Alcoholism can sometimes be treated by putting a substance into drinks to make the drinker sick.
  a How does this treatment try to stop someone drinking? Ⓗ Ⓢ Ⓦ
  b What sort of learning is this an example of?
2 Suggest why imprinting is important for the survival of young ducks.
3 Grizzly bears fish for salmon by leaping at them in the water. Older bears can catch more fish.
  a How is this learning useful to bears?
  b What sort of learning is this an example of?
4 Should experiments like those shown in A, B and C be carried out? Explain your reasoning. Ⓗ Ⓢ Ⓦ

⚠ *These young cranes were imprinted onto the hang glider of Angelo d'Arrigo (1961–2006). He taught them how to migrate!*

52 ●●●

If you need to find information about something, use the **index** on pages 191–192.

9Gd A world effort

Ⓗow Ⓢcience Ⓦorks

How can we try to reduce pollution and climate change?

Pollution and global warming are problems for everyone on the Earth. Pollution produced in one country can affect other countries. Global warming is likely to affect everyone in some way. Some people will be affected more than others.

The International Panel on Climate Change (IPCC) includes climate scientists and representatives from governments around the world. It looks at all the research carried out on climate change around the world. The IPCC produces reports at regular intervals, and governments use these reports to help them to decide what should be done to help to reduce the causes and effects of climate change.

We all need to try to do something to reduce pollution and global warming – but who should be doing most?

Cutting carbon emissions would damage our economy. Why should we cut our emissions while countries like India and China are increasing theirs?

Our economy is still developing. We cannot afford to spend money on cutting pollution or developing renewable energy resources. We deserve the same lifestyle as people in the West.

Each person in the US is responsible for about eight times as much carbon dioxide as each Chinese person. And nearly a third of our manufacturing is bought by the West!

We are not a rich country – we need to earn money from our rainforests. If you want us to stop clearing them, you must help us to get the money we need in other ways.

1 a Write down some natural sources of pollution.
  b Write down some sources of pollution caused by humans.
  c What effects can these different kinds of pollution have?
2 Suggest some ways in which pollution can be reduced.
3 Explain why pollution needs to be monitored.
4 a What causes global warming?
  b How could global warming affect us?

HAVE YOUR SAY
Who should take the responsibility for cutting greenhouse gas emissions?
Should developing nations be asked to cut their emissions?

90 ●●●

The **Have your say box** gives you an issue for a debate or discussion.

How to use this ActiveBook

Click on this tab to find all the electronic files on the ActiveBook.

Click this tab to see all the key words and what they mean. You can read them or you can click 'play' and listen to someone else read them out for you, to help with pronunciation.

Click on this tab at any time to search for help on how to use the ActiveBook.

Click on a section of the page and it will magnify, so that you can read it easily on screen. You can also zoom in on photos and diagrams on the page.

All of the questions in your book come with a level and some example answers, so you can see exactly how you're doing and how to improve. These are on your teacher's CD-ROM version of the book.

Click on any of the words in **bold** to see a box with the word and what it means. You can read them or you can click 'play' and listen to someone else read them out for you to help with pronunciation.

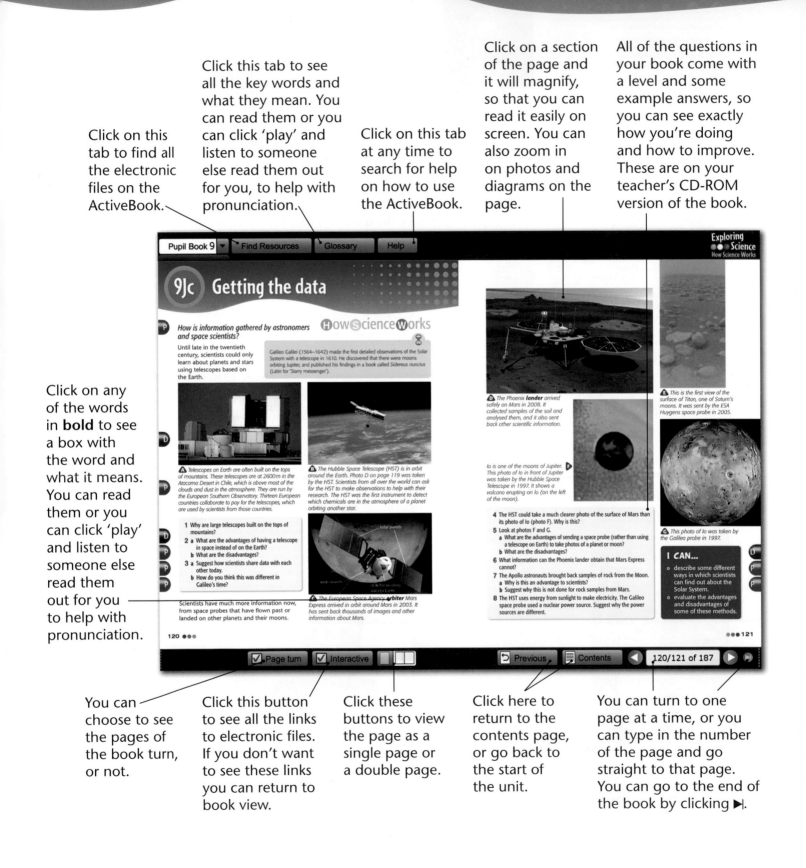

You can choose to see the pages of the book turn, or not.

Click this button to see all the links to electronic files. If you don't want to see these links you can return to book view.

Click these buttons to view the page as a single page or a double page.

Click here to return to the contents page, or go back to the start of the unit.

You can turn to one page at a time, or you can type in the number of the page and go straight to that page. You can go to the end of the book by clicking ▶|.

9Aa Science and imagination

HowScienceWorks

'Speculative fiction' involves things that are imagined. It covers many different styles including science fiction, horror and fantasy. Imagined organisms in speculative fiction are usually scientifically impossible but some are based on real life.

Centaurs appeared in Ancient Greek writing about 2500 years ago. They still appear in speculative fiction today (e.g. Harry Potter books). The idea for centaurs may have come from warriors on horseback invading areas where people had not learned to ride.

A Johannes Roberts directs speculative fiction films.

B A centaur from a fantasy film.

Centaurs are meant to be the result of mating a human with a horse. This is impossible. Horses and humans are different **species**. A species is a group of similar organisms that produce offspring that can also reproduce. Members of two different species cannot usually produce offspring. If they do, the offspring is called a **hybrid** and cannot reproduce.

Each individual has different **characteristics**. Your characteristics describe what you look like (e.g. your eye colour, skin colour, curliness of your hair). Differences in characteristics are called **variation**. There is a lot of variation between members of different species.

1 Describe four of your characteristics.
2 Describe how one characteristic varies between you and the person next to you.
3 Describe two characteristics of both monsters in photo C.
4 Photo D shows a zorse.
   a What is it a hybrid between?
   b Why is the zorse unable to reproduce?

C Characters in Star Wars: Return of the Jedi.

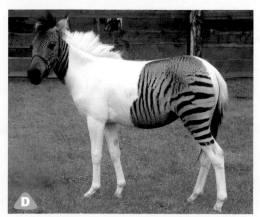

How do offspring inherit characteristics?

Characteristics that offspring get from their parents are **inherited**. The children in photo A have inherited the same eye colour from their father. However, the hair colours they have inherited show **variation**.

A

> 1 Look at photo A. Which parent has the girl inherited her hair colour from?

Film and TV programme makers often try to find child actors who have some features in common with the actors who play their parents. This is easier to do in cartoons!

> 2 a How is Fiona's face similar to her mother's?
> b List two features that Fergus has inherited from Frederick.

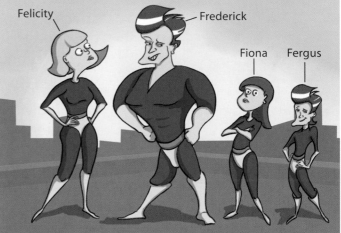

Felicity   Frederick   Fiona   Fergus

B The Fantastic family.

The **nuclei** of cells contain **chromosomes**, made from huge molecules of **DNA**. Chromosomes are divided into sections called **genes**. These genes carry the instructions (**genetic information**) that control your characteristics and how they vary. There are about 23 000 different genes in every human cell nucleus. Scientists are still trying to find out exactly how many.

> 3 Write a dictionary definition for 'genetic information'.

Many genes come in different forms. For example, a gene that causes eye colour may come in two types: one for brown eyes and one for blue.

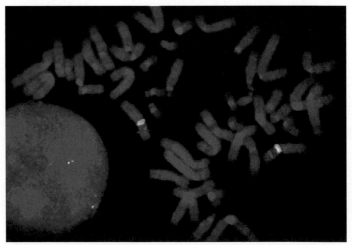

C The coloured patches show the positions of some genes on these chromosomes.

Fertilisation

Sex cells (or **gametes**) are specialised to transfer genes from parents to offspring. The nuclei of gametes only contain half the chromosomes of normal cells. In **fertilisation** *one* **sperm cell** enters an **ovum** (**egg cell**). The two nuclei **fuse** to form a nucleus with a complete set of genes.

The **fertilised egg cell** contains genes from both parents, and so the offspring inherits characteristics from both parents. Brothers and sisters look different because a person's gametes all contain a slightly different mix of their genes.

Each fertilised egg cell grows by **cell division** and forms an **embryo**. If cells in an early embryo split apart, identical twins are formed.

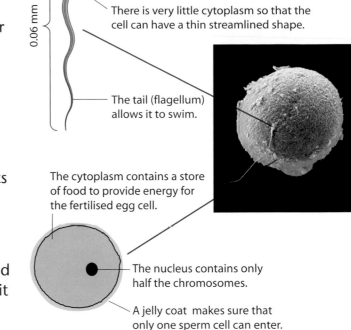

The tip of the head contains chemicals that attack the outside of the egg cell. This allows the sperm cell to burrow inside.

The nucleus contains only half the chromosomes.

There is very little cytoplasm so that the cell can have a thin streamlined shape.

0.06 mm

The tail (flagellum) allows it to swim.

The cytoplasm contains a store of food to provide energy for the fertilised egg cell.

The nucleus contains only half the chromosomes.

A jelly coat makes sure that only one sperm cell can enter.

D *Gametes are specialised.*

Mutations and superheroes

E

Changes in genes are called **mutations**. In science fiction, mutations can cause 'super powers'. The Incredible Hulk™ got his strength due to a mutation caused by nuclear radiation.

A German boy *inherited* a similar mutation to the Hulk! At age four he could hold 3 kg masses with his arms held out. However, this mutation has also made his heart muscles grow too big, which may cause serious problems.

4 Why do offspring get half their genes from each parent?

5 Why are brothers and sisters similar?

6 a How do identical twins form?
  b These twins are 'genetically identical'. What do you think this means?
  c How do you think the differences between identical twins are caused?

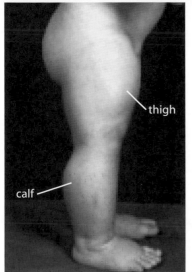

thigh

calf

F *The German boy at seven months old. Look at how well developed his calves and thigh muscles are.*

7 Some superheroes feel no pain. People with a certain mutation in their genes cannot feel pain either. Discuss the advantages and disadvantages of this. **H S W**

8 You can use an analogy to think about genetic information. A credit card has a chip and is in a wallet. What do those things represent in a cell? **H S W**

I CAN...

o recall how characteristics are inherited.
o recall what happens during human fertilisation.

How do chromosomes determine sex and some diseases?

There are 23 different types of human chromosome and every human cell has two of each type (46 altogether). The only exceptions to this are gametes, which have one of each type. When gametes join, the fertilised egg cell (or **zygote**) has a full set of 46 chromosomes.

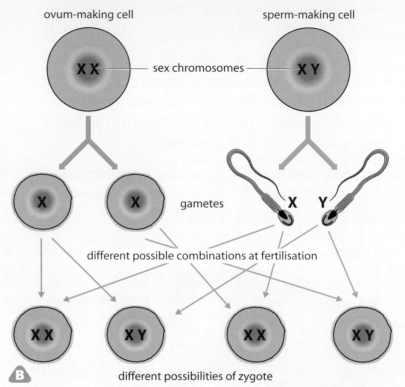

A Human chromosomes arranged in pairs and in order of size.

B different possibilities of zygote

1 How many chromosomes does the nucleus in each of these cells contain?
   a sperm cell   b ovum-making cell
   c nerve cell   d zygote

Chromosomes are numbered 1–22 and you have two of each type. The 23rd pair of chromosomes is slightly different. They are the **sex chromosomes**. A female cell nucleus contains two large 'X' sex chromosomes. A male nucleus contains one large 'X' and one small 'Y' sex chromosome.

2 Use diagram B to explain why about half of all babies born are male. **H S W**

3 Look at picture A. Are the chromosomes from a male or a female? Explain how you know. **H S W**

A pair of the same type of chromosomes will have the same genes. However, the genes may be slightly different. Different versions of the same gene are called **alleles** (pronounced 'al-*eels*').

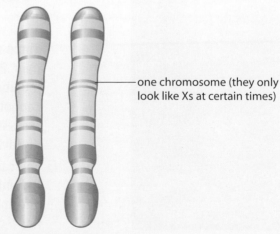

one chromosome (they only look like Xs at certain times)

C A model for the alleles for brown and blue eyes, which are found on chromosome 15. Scientists think this chromosome has 700–900 genes.

Gregor Mendel (1822–1884) was an Austrian monk who bred pea plants and discovered how features were inherited. He realised that certain 'factors' must be passed from parents to offspring. The word 'gene' was first used to describe Mendel's 'factors' in 1909, by Danish biologist Wilhelm Johannsen (1857–1927).

D Gregor Mendel.

Some alleles always have an effect and some alleles do not always have an effect. For instance, people who have the allele with the instruction 'brown eyes' will have brown eyes even if the other allele for eye colour has the instruction 'blue eyes'. The 'brown eyes' allele is **dominant**. The 'blue eyes' allele is **recessive**. For a recessive allele to have an effect, the alleles on both the chromosomes must be recessive.

Diagram E shows the possible eye colours of children born to parents who have different eye colours. We use letters to represent the alleles. Dominant alleles have a capital letter and recessive alleles have a small version of the *same* letter. So, the 'brown eyes' allele is 'B' and the 'blue eyes' allele is 'b'.

Sometimes alleles can cause **genetic diseases**. **Cystic fibrosis** is a genetic disease that damages the lungs and makes digesting food very difficult.

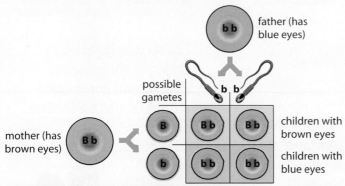

E A genetic cross diagram or **Punnett square**.

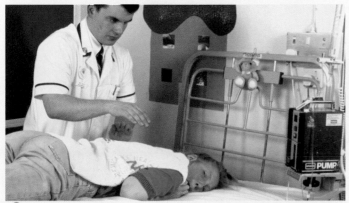

F A sticky fluid collects in the lungs of people with cystic fibrosis. Beating the back in a special way, followed by coughing, helps to clear the lungs.

4 What is a genetic disease?

5 What is a recessive allele?

6 Look at diagram E. Ⓗ Ⓢ Ⓦ
   a What percentage of this couple's children are likely to have brown eyes?
   b Redraw the diagram for a man with eye colour alleles Bb and a woman with alleles BB. What percentage of this couple's children would be likely to have brown eyes?
   c Redraw the diagram for a man and a woman who both have alleles Bb. What percentage of this couple's children are likely to have brown eyes?

7 Cystic fibrosis is caused by a recessive allele. Two parents are both **carriers** for the disease and both have alleles Cc (C is the normal allele, c is the allele that causes the disease). What percentage of children would they be likely to have with cystic fibrosis? Ⓗ Ⓢ Ⓦ

How does the environment cause variation?

Yellow Williams Red Williams (unripe) Red Williams (ripe) Green Anjou Bosc Comice Concorde Seckel

A Different varieties of pears.

Groups of plants that are the same **species** but show clear differences are from different **varieties**.

Differences in shape and colour are easy to spot but not all characteristics can be seen. For instance, Green Anjou trees are less likely than Red Williams trees to get a disease called fireblight, which kills the leaves. The Green Anjou trees are more **resistant** to the disease.

> 1 State two variations of pears that are controlled by genes that:
> a can be seen b cannot be seen.

Just as plants have different varieties, a species of animal can have different **breeds**. Highland cattle have long hair and can live easily in the Scottish mountains. Boran cattle have a high number of sweat glands and so can live easily in Africa.

H S W

Do you think there are more differences between apples of the same variety or between separate varieties of apple?
o How would you test your prediction?

2 Explain why Highland cattle are not farmed in Ethiopia and Boran cattle are not farmed on Scottish mountains.

B Highland cattle.

C Boran cattle.

D Skin colour is caused by genes and environmental factors. Darker skin is less likely to be damaged by strong sunshine.

It is not just genes that cause variation. **Environmental variations** are caused by **environmental factors** (things in the surroundings). However, many variations have environmental *and* genetic causes.

3 State one variation of pear trees and the environmental factor that causes it.

4 a What environmental factor causes a suntan?
   b Suggest an environmental factor that can cause scars.
   c Describe two of your environmental variations.

Environmental factors and genes can both affect life processes. Here are some examples.

Movement: Arthritis is when your joints become painful and swell up. It is more common in older people. The causes are not fully understood but some people have genes that make them more likely to get the condition. Injuries or joint infections can also cause it.

Reproduction: The genes found in **hybrid** animals mean that they cannot reproduce.

Sensitivity: The plants in photo F have been grown in near darkness. The shoots have grown quickly and bend towards the small amount of light. This growth helps the plant to find enough light for photosynthesis.

Growth: Potatoes of the same variety can come in many shapes and sizes. Larger ones grow in areas with just the right amounts of light, water and mineral salts.

Respiration: Some weedkillers kill plants by stopping respiration occurring in them.

Excretion: Sweating cools you down but can also remove waste substances from your body, like urea, which is normally found in urine! Most humans sweat when sitting still if the air temperature is above about 30 °C. Camels only sweat when the temperature reaches 41 °C.

E *This liger cannot reproduce.*

F

Nutrition: Many diseases of plants stop them photosynthesising, so they cannot make enough food for themselves.

5 For each life process in the coloured box, state whether the variation is:
   a caused by genes, by environmental factors or by both.
   b helpful or unhelpful to the organism concerned, giving your reasons.

6 Write down whether the following characteristics are caused by genes, environmental factors or both.
   having naturally blue eyes   having a scar   having naturally curly hair   being very tall   having a cold   being able to speak French

I CAN...
o describe variations caused by environmental factors, genes or both.
o explain how variations can have benefits and drawbacks.

How do humans alter animal characteristics?

There are about 150 breeds of dog but they are all the same species. Photo A shows some different breeds.

> **1 a** Name one difference between Labradors and Shih-tzus.
> **b** Name two characteristics that the two breeds share.

Yellow Labrador Retriever

Border Collie

English Springer Spaniel

Shih-Tzu

A

Some animals have characteristics that make them useful to humans. For example, a greyhound owner wants fast greyhounds. Very fast dogs are mated with each other. The offspring should also be fast runners. The fastest of the offspring are then mated with other very fast greyhounds, which will hopefully produce even faster dogs. This process is called **selective breeding** because only animals with certain characteristics are selected for **breeding**.

> **2** Suggest two characteristics dog breeders may select for.

Modern breeds of sheep have been selectively bred from mouflon sheep. Mouflon sheep are hairy and have fatty meat. Over thousands of years, farmers have selectively bred new breeds of sheep with characteristics that humans want.

Different breeds of an animal may be mated with each other to produce offspring with characteristics from both breeds. This is called **cross-breeding**.

Mouflon sheep

Merino sheep have been selectively bred for wool.

B

 +  →

Friesian cows are good for milking.

The Hereford breed produces good meat.

Hereford–Friesian crosses produce good beef and milk.

C

> **3** Look at photo C. ⒽⓈⓌ
> **a** Why do farmers produce Hereford–Friesian crosses?
> **b** Which visible characteristic have the crosses inherited from each breed?
> **4** Suggest two characteristics a farmer may select when breeding:
> **a** sheep. **b** chickens.
> **c** pigs.

Send in the clones

When animals mate, their gametes only contain half their genes and so the genes for useful characteristics may not be passed on to the offspring. It would be useful to create exact copies of animals and this can be done using **cloning**.

Diagram D shows how a sheep was cloned. Cloning is still very expensive and difficult to do but many scientists think that it will become quite common.

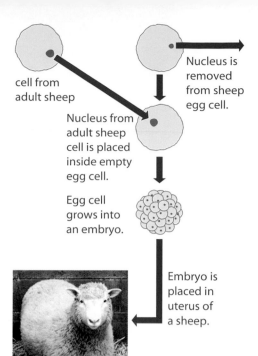

cell from adult sheep

Nucleus is removed from sheep egg cell.

Nucleus from adult sheep cell is placed inside empty egg cell.

Egg cell grows into an embryo.

Embryo is placed in uterus of a sheep.

D *Dolly the sheep (1996–2003) was a* **clone** *– an exact copy of another sheep.*

5 In the Star Wars® series of films, a fearsome warrior called Jango Fett is cloned to create an army. **H S W**
   a What is the advantage of creating an army this way?
   b Suggest a disadvantage.
   c If you were to create a clone army, what characteristics would you want the clones to have?
6 Although clones have exactly the same genes, there are often differences between them. Suggest why this is.

Here comes spidergoat!

The goats in photo E produce spider silk in their milk. They have been **genetically modified**. Scientists took the spider silk gene from a golden orb weaver spider and managed to put it into the DNA of a goat. This goat was then cloned. The goats are milked and the spider silk is used to make BioSteel® – a material that is much lighter and stronger than steel.

Spiderman® gained his powers when bitten by a radioactive spider, which caused genetic modification. 'Spidergoats', however, can't swing from buildings.

E

7 What is genetic modification?
8 Spiderman® can shoot webs from the palms of his hands. Suggest one *genetic* reason why the goats cannot do this.
9 Design your own genetically modified superhero. **H S W**

I CAN...

o describe how and why we selectively breed some animals. **H S W**
o recall what a clone is.
o describe what a genetically modified organism is.

How are plants bred?

Triffids are highly dangerous plants that use their roots to walk. They also have a highly poisonous sting in their flowers, which can shoot out and kill people. It is thought that the plants were created in Russia using genetic modification.

Fortunately, triffids don't exist. They are from a book called *The Day of the Triffids* by John Wyndham.

> **1 a** Write down two characteristics of triffids.
> **b** Suggest an organism from which a gene for each characteristic might have come.
> **2** All organisms move.
> **a** State one similarity in the way that *real* plants and animals move.
> **b** State one difference.

Scientists have created genetically modified (**GM**) sweetcorn that kills insects that normally eat it, GM tomatoes that last a long time and GM rice that contains lots of vitamin A. Some people think that growing and eating GM plants could be dangerous because GM plants have genes that they do not naturally contain.

A Triffids.

beefsteak tomato

plum tomato

cherry tomato

pear tomato

C These tomato varieties were developed using selective and cross-breeding.

> **3 a** Why are some people against GM crops? **H S W**
> **b** Suggest why some people are in favour of GM crops. **H S W**

Plant breeders still also use traditional selective breeding and cross-breeding methods to create new varieties.

B Protesters destroying GM oilseed rape.

> **!**
> Carrots used to be white or purple. They are orange today because a sixteenth century Dutch plant breeder selectively bred carrots from plants with a mutation that made them orange – the colour of the Dutch Royal family!

4 Suggest three characteristics that vary between different tomato varieties. Ⓗ Ⓢ Ⓦ

5 Suggest one characteristic that was selected when breeding beefsteak tomatoes. Ⓗ Ⓢ Ⓦ

Ⓗ Ⓢ Ⓦ

How would you investigate whether selective breeding of pea plants has produced peas with different characteristics?

○ What characteristics would you investigate?

To breed plants together, plant breeders take **pollen grains** (the male gametes) from one plant and place them on a **stigma** of another flower. This transfer of pollen is called **pollination**. Pollen is usually carried by the wind or on the bodies of insects.

A pollen grain grows a **pollen tube** down into the **ovary** of the flower. Here the tube enters an **ovule**, which contains an ovum (egg cell). The nucleus from the pollen grain enters the ovum. This is fertilisation. The fertilised egg cell turns into part of a **seed**.

6 What are the male and female gametes (sex cells) in a plant called?

7 How does a plant breeder make sure that only pollen from one flower pollinates another flower?

8 Write a set of instructions on how to cross-breed plants. Ⓗ Ⓢ Ⓦ

The **anthers** of a flower are cut off.

Pollen from the anthers of another flower is brushed onto the stigma.

The flower is placed in a plastic bag, so that pollen from other flowers cannot get to it.

Ⓓ *A plant breeder cross-breeding roses.*

Cloning

Many plants can clone themselves! This is called **asexual reproduction**, and does not need gametes. Instead, part of the parent plant forms a new plant. For example strawberries grow runners from which new plants grow.

Gardeners and plant breeders use asexual reproduction to produce plant clones quickly. They cut a side stem from a plant and place it in moist soil. Eventually, the stem sprouts roots and forms a new plant. This is called 'taking a cutting'.

runner

Ⓔ

9 a Suggest an advantage of asexual reproduction for plants.
   b Suggest a disadvantage.

10 Why can't plant breeders use asexual reproduction to create new varieties?

I CAN...

○ describe how plants reproduce sexually and asexually.

○ consider the advantages and disadvantages of genetic modification. Ⓗ Ⓢ Ⓦ

Why are some people against artificial breeding?

The idea of genetic and breeding experiments going wrong is found in a lot of speculative fiction.

Some people fear that such fictional disasters might become a reality. For instance, GM bacteria might escape from labs and cause diseases. However, GM bacteria are already used to produce substances like insulin for diabetics, and GM plants could provide poor people with more food.

B *Pugs often suffer from breathing problems.*

C *When Bernann McKinney's bull terrier died, she went to South Korea to get him cloned from cells taken from his ear. It cost her about £25 000.*

HowScienceWorks

A *In this 1959 film, a failed genetic modification medical treatment results in a man becoming half alligator!*

Selective breeding has been used for thousands of years to produce a huge range of plant varieties. Selective breeding (e.g. of dogs) also provides work and pleasure, but can result in problems for certain breeds.

Cloning plants can also cause problems. In areas planted with identical plants, one disease can kill all of them because there is no variation in their disease-resistance characteristics.

In the last 20 years, cloned mammals have become a reality but a very expensive one. Some scientists think that this technology could soon be used to create copies of ourselves, maybe to produce spare body parts.

HAVE YOUR SAY

Some people think that genetic modification should be banned. What do you think about this idea?

1 List one benefit and one drawback of using:
   a selective breeding   b genetic modification   c cloning.
2 Describe two breeds or varieties that might be made using genetic modification. Describe what these organisms would be able to do and why this would be helpful.
3 Using examples from this unit, suggest some ways in which ordinary people can change how science is used.

A model life

How Science Works

Social behaviour is how an animal reacts to animals of the same species. Companies often try to change your behaviour by using happy, healthy, fit and active models in their adverts. This is to make you link a product with feeling good. The advertisers hope that this link will make you buy the product.

1 Look at photo A. What is the link that the advertiser is trying to get you to make?
2 a What change in your behaviour do advertisers want you to make?
 b Suggest one way in which this might be a good thing.

A

B

Models advertise everything from expensive clothes, jewellery and cars, to everyday foods, nappies and toys. Different products need different models. Food companies choose fit and active-looking models. Very thin and attractive models are often used to advertise expensive clothes.

3 What sort of model would you choose to advertise the following?
 a nappies   b a sunshine holiday   c toy cars
 d milkshakes to replace meals, for people going on a diet
 e a weightlifting exercise machine

Simon is a model. He is often used to advertise sports merchandise. To keep getting jobs, he needs to make sure that his body shape remains the same and that he looks after his skin and nails. Many of the products that he uses are the result of scientific research (e.g. skincare lotions).

4 a How do you think exercise machines are scientifically tested? Think of as many ways as you can.
 b What are the benefits of buying an exercise machine?
 c What are the drawbacks?
 d Use your answers to parts **b** and **c** to evaluate exercise machines. That means you need to say whether you think exercise machines are worthwhile or not.

C Simon Greenwood.

What do we mean by fitness?

Most models in advertising look 'fit'. Being 'fit' means that your body is able to do the activities that your lifestyle demands. This may include being able to run upstairs without getting out of breath or being strong enough to lift things.

A

B

C

1 a Look at the photos of models A–C. Which model do you think is the fittest?
b Why do you think this?

Fitness therefore means different things to different people. To look at fitness in more detail we divide it into four **S-factors: suppleness, strength, speed** and **stamina** (how long you can do something for). Simon uses a fitness programme that includes work on all four S-factors.

D

Weekly fitness programme

Mon: stretch, chest weights, long run
Tues: stretch, arm weights, sprint intervals
Weds: stretch, general weights
Thurs: stretch, back weights, long run
Fri: stretch, leg weights
Sat: rest
Sun: stretch, long run

Diet: balanced, with plenty of fibre and water

plenty of sleep ✓
smoking ✗
drug taking ✗
alcohol - in moderation

2 Look at this list of sports.
archery   cricket   fishing
hill walking   volleyball
Which sport do you think requires:
a the most stamina
b the least stamina?

3 What exercises does Simon do to increase his performance in each S-factor?

4 a Look at photo B. Which S-factor would this model score highest in?
b Which S-factor would you score highest in?

Just being able to do everyday activities does not give you any idea of *how* fit you are. Scientists use rules or **criteria** to judge how fit someone is. For example, how fast you run can be used as a criterion to judge your fitness.

Fitness programmes help to keep your body's **organ systems** working properly. The **circulatory**, **digestive** and **breathing** (**respiratory**) **systems** work to provide muscles with glucose and oxygen during exercise. All the cells in your body use **aerobic respiration** to release energy from glucose.

glucose + oxygen → water + carbon dioxide

The speed criterion for the men's British Olympic 100 m team is that they must be able to run 100 m in less than 10.21 seconds.

When you exercise, your cells need to respire more. Corneille Heymans (1892–1968) discovered that nerves control the amount of respiration occurring in your cells.

The glucose comes from carbohydrates digested in your digestive system. It is carried in the blood to all your cells by the circulatory system. Oxygen is taken into your body by the breathing system and also carried around your body by the circulatory system.

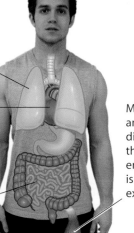

Lungs take oxygen from the air.

The heart pumps blood carrying oxygen and glucose around your body.

The small intestine digests and absorbs food.

Muscles take oxygen and glucose (from digested food) out of the blood to release energy. More energy is needed when you exercise.

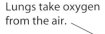

Exercise makes your heart muscles stronger so that it pumps more blood with each beat. People with high stamina have slower resting **heartbeat rates**. When you get fitter, by improving your stamina, your resting heartbeat rate gets slower. Your heartbeat rate also returns to normal more quickly after exercise when you are fitter.

These are both criteria used to evaluate whether a fitness programme is working.

5 Describe two criteria used to evaluate fitness programmes.

6 Here is a list of organ systems:
circulatory system   breathing system
digestive system   nervous system
locomotor system (skeleton, muscles and joints)
Which organ system does each part of Simon's training programme help?

7 For each organ labelled in photo E, write down the organ system it is part of.

8 How does knowing about the effects of exercise help people to make decisions about looking after their bodies?   **H S W**

How would you measure your speed, strength and stamina?

I CAN...

o recall the benefits of exercise.
o recall how different organ systems work together.
o use criteria to judge things.   **H S W**

How does the breathing system work?

Cells in the tubes leading to your lungs produce **mucus** to trap dirt and microbes. The mucus is swept out of the tubes by **cilia** on **ciliated epithelial cells**.

Many people think that mucus can cause a stuffy nose. In fact, stuffiness is caused by swollen blood vessels, which make the tubes at the back of your nose narrower. Decongestants are medicines that reduce the swelling.

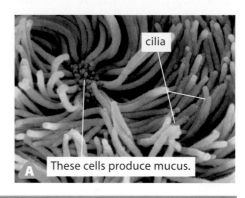
A These cells produce mucus.

> 1 What sort of model would you select to advertise a decongestant?
> 2 Explain why using the medicine in photo B will help you breathe more easily. Ⓗ Ⓢ Ⓦ

Your nose is where air normally enters your breathing system. The breathing system absorbs oxygen and excretes (gets rid of) carbon dioxide. This is called **gas exchange**.

The breathing system contains the lungs, bronchi, trachea and **diaphragm** ('*dye-a-fram*'). The diaphragm is a sheet of muscle.

Don't let a cold turn your world upside down.
Breathe again with
Naseby Decongestant capsules
B

> 3 Explain the meanings of:
>   a breathing b gas exchange c ventilation.
> 4 When you inhale do your lungs get bigger or smaller?
> 5 How do the muscles and diaphragm cause you to exhale?
> 6 Diagram D shows a model of the breathing system. When the rubber sheet is pulled down, the volume inside the jar increases and air is forced into the balloons. Ⓗ Ⓢ Ⓦ
>   a What happens when the rubber sheet is let go?
>   b What part does the rubber sheet represent?

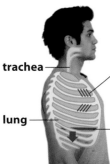
trachea
lung

Muscles between the ribs contract and pull ribs up and out.
The diaphragm relaxes and rises.
The diaphragm contracts and moves down.
Breathing in (inhalation).

Muscles relax and the ribs move back down.
Breathing out (exhalation).

C

D

Diagram C shows how your diaphragm and other muscles change the volume of your chest, which is called **breathing**. This causes air to flow into and out of your lungs. The flow of air is called **ventilation**.

I CAN...

o recall how ventilation occurs.

Why are fewer people smoking?

How Science Works

Tobacco smoke damages the breathing and circulatory systems. **Nicotine** makes arteries narrower. Carbon monoxide stops red blood cells carrying oxygen. This can cause babies to be **premature** if pregnant women smoke. **Tar** causes lung damage and **lung cancer**.

Cigarettes used to be fashionable and many products were advertised showing glamorous models smoking. In February 2003 tobacco advertising became illegal in the UK.

A

> **1** List three chemicals in cigarette smoke and describe their dangers.

Today, advertising tries to stop people smoking. In January 2004 the British Heart Foundation spent £4 million on a campaign showing fat oozing out of cigarettes and smokers' blood vessels. Smoking can cause fat to build up in arteries and block them. This can stop blood reaching the brain (causing a **stroke**) and heart (causing a **heart attack**).

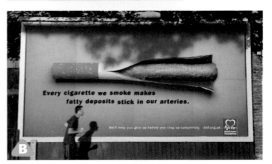

B

Doctors also help people to stop smoking. Chart C shows the numbers of people who stopped smoking using the NHS.

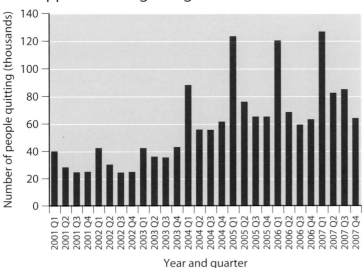

c People in England who used the NHS to stop smoking. A quarter is a quarter of a year = 3 months. So Q1 is January–March.

2 a Describe the overall trend shown in chart C.
  b What do you think is responsible for this trend?
  c Tom has an opinion: 'The number of people quitting smoking has not changed for a long time.' How would you use evidence from the chart to *support* his statement?
  d Describe the repeating pattern in the chart.
  e Why do you think this pattern occurs?
  f Do you think the advertising ban or the BHF adverts had more impact? Use the chart to support your argument.

I CAN...

- recall some effects of smoking on the body.
- identify patterns and trends in data, and suggest causes.
- explain how data can be manipulated.

Why do we need a balanced diet?

Dieticians can help models to plan **balanced diets**. However, there are pressures on some models to remain very thin. This can cause diseases like **anorexia**, when someone is convinced that they are fat and stops eating.

Anorexia can cause **deficiency diseases** – diseases caused by a lack of a **nutrient**. However, taking too much of a nutrient can also be dangerous. Some people make themselves ill by taking too many vitamin and mineral pills, instead of eating properly.

Nutrient	Recommended daily amount for 14-year-olds	Deficiency disease	Problems if too much eaten
protein	42.1g (boys) 41.2g (girls)	**kwashiorkor** – swollen tummy, liver damage	–
calcium	1000 mg (boys) 800 mg (girls)	**rickets** – weak bones with odd shapes	damage to kidneys
iron	11.3 mg (boys) 14.8 mg (girls)	**anaemia** – tiredness and shortness of breath	damage to heart and liver
vitamin A	600 μg	liver damage and **night-blindness** – inability to see in dim light	general tissue damage, loss of coordination
vitamin C	35 mg	**scurvy** – bleeding gums.	–

B *Data from British Nutrition Foundation. 1 g = 1000 mg. 1 mg = 1000 μg.*

1 Why do you think many models suffer from anorexia?
2 a Why do you think children are more likely than adults to be poisoned by vitamin and mineral pills?
  b Suggest ways in which these poisonings could be prevented. Ⓗ Ⓢ Ⓦ
3 Vitamin and mineral pills were invented in the 1930s. Ⓗ Ⓢ Ⓦ
  a Why do you think companies started to sell them?
  b What are the benefits and drawbacks of this scientific advance?
4 A child's liver is badly damaged.
  a Suggest how not eating the correct balance of nutrients can cause this.
  b What could be done to save the child? Ⓗ Ⓢ Ⓦ

! In the USA in the 1990s, 28 children died of iron poisoning, mainly due to eating vitamin and mineral tablets that they thought were sweets.

A *Luisel Ramos died of heart failure during a fashion show. It is said that she consumed only lettuce and diet drinks for weeks beforehand. She was 22.*

! Polar bear and husky dog livers contain so much vitamin A that they are poisonous. In 1913, Antarctic explorer Xavier Mertz died from eating his sledge dogs' livers.

DCPIP is a blue chemical that turns colourless when drops of vitamin C are added to it.
○ How would you find out whether vitamin C is affected by cooking?

I CAN...

○ recognise that nutrients are important in the correct amounts.

How can evidence be misleading?

HowScienceWorks

Dieting is very popular. There are thousands of diet books for sale and many of these sell millions of copies. If your food contains more energy than you need, some is stored as fat. 'Low calorie diets' get you to eat foods containing less energy. Other diets get you to eat very little of one type of food, do lots of exercise or take pills to control your appetite.

Many diets give 'evidence' that they work. The evidence for Diet A 'explains' how it is meant to work, using scientific words. However, there are no investigation results to show that it does work.

'Evidence' in graphs and charts may mean nothing. Your 'energy level' is measured in Graph B but energy level is only a feeling,

People in the UK spend about £350 million each year on dieting.

Diet A works because it burns up fat by switching your cells into lipolysis mode. Cellular fats are converted into ketones, which you excrete in your urine.

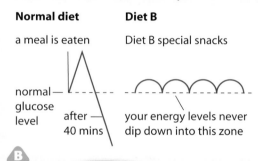

Normal diet — a meal is eaten, normal glucose level, after 40 mins

Diet B — Diet B special snacks, your energy levels never dip down into this zone

B

not something that can be measured. And most people have bodies that keep blood glucose levels within a very narrow range.

Some 'evidence' can mislead you. Diet C makes a true statement but one that is misleading.

A

The percentage of fat in the diets of our study group was decreased and yet the members of the group got fatter. So eating fat does not make you fat. Diet C advises you to eat fat but not carbohydrate.

C *The percentage of fat may have decreased but not the actual amount of fat eaten.*

1 Write three bullet points to give advice to people looking for a diet.
2 Vitamins A, D, E and K are fat-soluble.
   a What do you think fat-soluble means?
   b Suggest a problem with going on a very low-fat diet.
3 Make up some figures to illustrate how a percentage can be used to hide a real figure. Carefully show your working.
4 How would you collect evidence to show that a diet plan works?
5 Why are people tempted to give misleading evidence when marketing diet plans?
6 Explain why many diet plans use lots of scientific words.
7 In the Slim-Fast® diet you replace one meal a day with a special milkshake. What are the benefits and drawbacks of this diet?

How do drugs affect our bodies?

Drugs are substances that affect the way your body works. Some drugs are **medicines** but all drugs can have harmful or unpleasant effects (**side-effects**) and many are **addictive** (which means that people feel that they can't cope without them).

Aspirin and ibuprofen are medicines that reduce pain and swelling. These can be bought 'over the counter'. Others, like antibiotics, have to be prescribed by a doctor.

Recreational drugs are taken for pleasure. **Caffeine**, nicotine and alcohol are legal recreational drugs. Others are illegal because they have bad side-effects. **Cannabis** can cause memory loss. **Ecstasy** can cause mental illness, kidney problems, and even death. **Cocaine** is addictive and can cause blocked arteries. **Heroin** is also addictive. It can cause collapsed veins, vomiting and severe headaches.

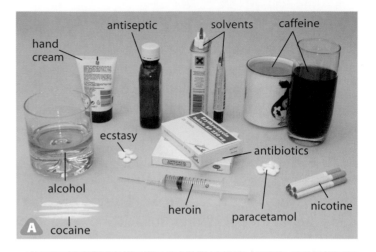

A

1 a Use photo A to make two lists – one of drugs and one of other substances.
  b Divide your list of drugs into further groups. Explain your reasoning. **H** **S** **W**

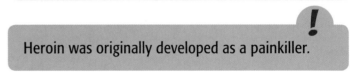

Heroin was originally developed as a painkiller.

2 Look at photo A again.
  a Which of the substances do you think are harmful?
  b Which can you buy at any age?
  c Which are only legal to buy above a certain age?
  d Which are illegal?

Stimulants

Drugs often act on **neurons** (nerve cells) in the nervous system. Substances that increase the speed that neurons carry electrical signals (**impulses**) are called **stimulants**. Nicotine, caffeine, cocaine and ecstasy are examples.

3 What do stimulants do?
4 Why do people continue using cocaine even after it starts to harm them?

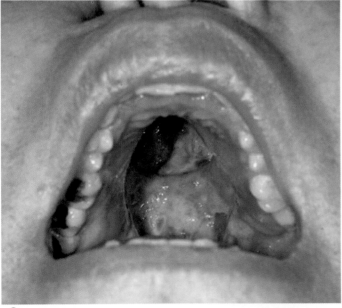

B Cocaine has made a hole in the roof of this man's mouth. Some models use the drug because it can reduce hunger.

How could you find out if caffeine makes you more alert?

small alcopop = 1.5 units

pint of beer = 3 units

a measure of spirits = 1.5 units

glass of red wine = 2.5 units

D Alcohol is measured in units. Men are advised not to drink more than 21 units a week, and women no more than 14 units.

Depressants

Drugs that slow neurons down are called **depressants**. Heroin and the **solvents** found in glues and paints are dangerous depressants. Solvents can stop the heart and lungs working, and cause severe brain damage. Sniffing solvents is called **solvent abuse**.

Large quantities of alcohol can change a person's behaviour. People become loud and even aggressive because alcohol stops neurons in the brain working, including those that control behaviour. Too much alcohol causes vomiting. In very large amounts, it can cause death because it stops the brain sending impulses to the lungs and so breathing stops.

Drinking heavily for a long time can cause brain damage. Alcohol also stops the body absorbing and storing vitamins and minerals. This can cause deficiency diseases.

All drugs can cause liver damage because this organ breaks them down. For example, an average liver breaks down about one unit of alcohol per hour.

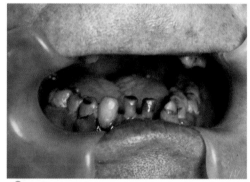

E This man has scurvy due to a lack of vitamin C caused by heavy drinking.

5 Why do you think people should not drink and drive? **H S W**

6 A man drank a pint of beer and a measure of whisky. **H S W**
   a How many units of alcohol did he drink?
   b How long would it take his liver to break this down?
   c If he drank this amount every day, how many units above the recommended weekly amount would he drink?

7 Copy and complete this table. **H S W**

Name of drug	Stimulant or depressant?	Side-effects

G

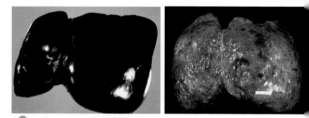

F The liver on the left is healthy. The one on the right has been damaged by alcohol.

I CAN...

o recall how drugs affect the body.

What else do people do to look after themselves?

Advertisers look through many photographs of models searching for the perfect body shape to advertise their product. So, it is important for models to keep their bodies looking like their photographs! Models with muscles need to keep them.

1 a How would you describe Simon's body to an advertiser?
b Suggest a product you think Simon could advertise.

The bones of your **skeleton** have three main functions:
- support (e.g. the **vertebrae** in your '**backbone**' hold you up).
- protection (e.g. your **skull** protects your brain).
- movement (using muscles).

A Simon has muscles!

! A human adult skeleton has 206 bones. The smallest is the stirrup bone in the ear, which is about the size of a grain of rice. The largest is the hip bone.

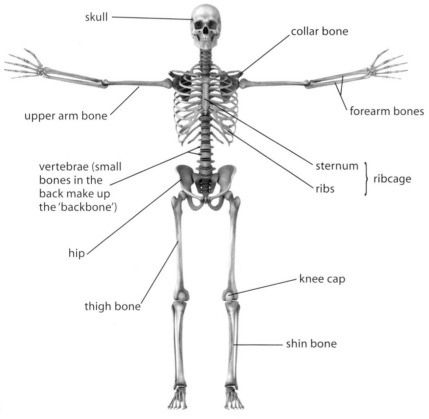

skull
collar bone
upper arm bone
forearm bones
vertebrae (small bones in the back make up the 'backbone')
sternum
ribs } ribcage
hip
knee cap
thigh bone
shin bone

B

2 Which bones protect the heart and lungs?

3 The nervous system contains the brain and spinal cord. Your spinal cord runs down your back and contains many important nerves. Which bones protect:
a your brain?
b your spinal cord?

4 What does your body use to make bones move?

Together your bones and muscles form your locomotor system. Like most of our organ systems, exercise is important for keeping this system healthy. Exercise keeps muscles strong. If a muscle gets very much stronger it often becomes bigger.

Many people think that your skeleton stops growing when you are an adult. This is not true. Many of your bones are constantly changing shape to adapt to your lifestyle. People who do manual labour or who work out a lot develop thick arm bones, to support bigger muscles.

Evidence that bones grow also comes from looking at how broken bones repair. If you break a bone, the two ends are put in the correct position and then placed in a cast. After a couple of months, new bone grows and mends the break.

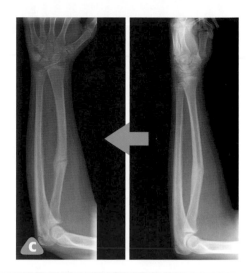

Carry out a survey to find out:
o which bone is the most commonly broken.
o how long different bones take to mend.
Find some secondary source data. Explain why there are differences between the secondary source and your findings.

Simon has well-developed **biceps** muscles. He uses bicep curls to help keep them in shape. Muscles move bones at **joints** by getting shorter and fatter (they **contract**). When they stop contracting they **relax**. Muscles can only pull and cannot push. So, they have to work in **antagonistic pairs** to be able to move bones back and forth. The biceps and **triceps** muscles are an antagonistic pair, which move the lower arm.

5 The diagrams show the names that doctors give to different sorts of break. What sort of break is shown in X-ray C?

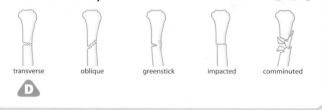

transverse   oblique   greenstick   impacted   comminuted

D

6 When the biceps muscle contracts, what happens to the triceps?

7 Why do muscles work in antagonistic pairs?

8 Look at drawing F. It shows some other muscles in the body. You don't need to remember their names!
  a Write down all the antagonistic pairs you can see.
  b If you point your toes to the ground, which muscle contracts?
  c If you raise your toes, which muscle contracts?

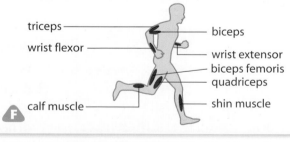

triceps — biceps
wrist flexor — wrist extensor
— biceps femoris
— quadriceps
calf muscle — shin muscle

F

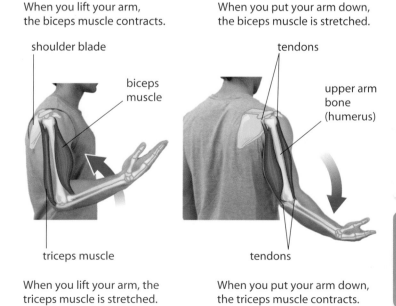

When you lift your arm, the biceps muscle contracts.

When you put your arm down, the biceps muscle is stretched.

shoulder blade

tendons

biceps muscle

upper arm bone (humerus)

triceps muscle

tendons

When you lift your arm, the triceps muscle is stretched.

When you put your arm down, the triceps muscle contracts.

E

I CAN...

o recall how the skeleton carries out its functions.

HowScienceWorks

Is advertising using models a good thing?

H. G. Wells (1866–1946) was a famous writer. He once said that 'advertising is legalised lying'. Some people agree and want to put stricter controls on how models are used to advertise things.

A Beltham chocolate is always a special occasion.

(but you don't need to dress up)

A

A Beltham chocolate is always a special occasion.

and you don't need to dress up!

If people see only adverts of thin people eating chocolate they will think that chocolate makes you thin. We need to make advertisers show a range of sizes of models advertising chocolates.

Silkreem hands

discover your silky side...

B

This advert features a 'hand model' – someone who looks after her hands very, very well especially to appear in adverts like this. It will make people think that they can easily get their hands to look like this. We need to show more realistic hands.

Silkreem hands
for the real you.

HAVE YOUR SAY

New scientific developments are constantly being made and incorporated into new products, which are then advertised for sale. Do you think that some or all advertisers should be forced to use more realistic people in their adverts?

1 Do you think that H. G. Wells was right? Explain your reasoning.

2 What things should people remember when they look at adverts? Write a list.

3 Briefly state how you can keep the following organ systems healthy:
   a digestive system   b breathing system   c circulatory system
   d nervous system   e locomotor system (your muscles and bones)

4 a In which organ system do you think the specialised cell in drawing C is found?
   b What do these cells do?

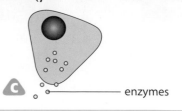

C   enzymes

A farmer's life

HowScienceWorks

Farmers use **criteria** to judge whether it is worthwhile to farm an organism. Criteria are a set of rules used to judge how good or bad something is. Some criteria that a farmer may use are:
• Will it make money?
• Will it harm the environment?
• Will it affect my family life?

Money

The costs of growing crops include seeds, machinery, fertiliser, pesticides, diesel and wages for workers. Chris then needs to know how much the crop can be sold for. The values of crops go up and down, so he may not be sure how much money he will get when the crop is sold.

A Chris Page farms both plants and animals in Oxfordshire.

B Wheat is a common crop.

Over the years, the amount of wheat that is being grown has increased. This is because there is a high demand. Wheat is used for animal feed, for foods (like bread) and to make biofuels.

Environment

Some farmers try to avoid harming the environment by using very few chemicals. This is known as **organic farming**.

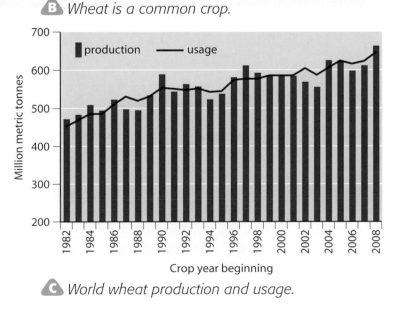
C World wheat production and usage.

1 Dairy farming can mean that the farmer has to get up at 4 o'clock every morning to milk the cows. Suggest some reasons why a farmer might decide against setting up a dairy farm.

2 a Explain what effect a lot of cloudy weather during a year would have on the amount of wheat that is harvested.
  b How will this affect the price?

3 Look at graph C. Suggest one year in which the price of wheat was:
  a high b low.

4 Explain your choices for question 3.

9Ca Plant reactions

What chemical reactions happen in a plant?

The Greek scientist Aristotle (384 BCE–322 BCE) thought that plants ate soil and used their roots to suck it up. Some people believed this until Belgian scientist Jean-Baptiste van Helmont (1579–1644) did the experiment in diagram A.

> 1 How do van Helmont's results provide evidence to disprove Aristotle's theory? Ⓗ Ⓢ Ⓦ
>
> 2 Some people suggested that the extra mass of the tree came from the water that he added. Was this a sensible suggestion? Explain your answer. Ⓗ Ⓢ Ⓦ

Today we know that plants make their own food using carbon dioxide and water. These are the **raw materials** (**reactants**) for **photosynthesis**. The **products** are a sugar, called **glucose**, and oxygen. We can show what happens in a **word equation**.

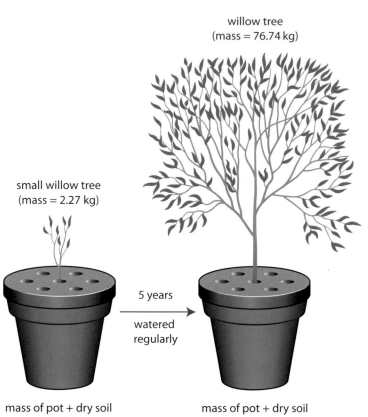

willow tree
(mass = 76.74 kg)

small willow tree
(mass = 2.27 kg)

5 years

watered regularly

mass of pot + dry soil
= 90.72 kg

mass of pot + dry soil
= 90.66 kg

Ⓐ

$$\underset{(CO_2)}{\textbf{carbon dioxide}} + \underset{(H_2O)}{\textbf{water}} \xrightarrow[\text{chlorophyll}]{\text{light energy}} \underset{(C_6H_{12}O_6)}{\textbf{glucose}} + \underset{(O_2)}{\textbf{oxygen}}$$

Light energy is needed to make photosynthesis happen. A substance called **chlorophyll**, found inside **chloroplasts** in plant cells, captures the light energy. The light energy is transferred to chemical energy, which is stored in the glucose. If a factor like the amount of light or a raw material is in short supply, photosynthesis will not happen as fast as it can. The factor is said to be a **limiting factor**.

> 3 Why do plants in a field only photosynthesise during the day?
> 4 Why are these not reactants? a light   b chlorophyll
> 5 In what part of a plant cell does photosynthesis occur?

> Ⓗ Ⓢ Ⓦ
> Canadian pondweed will produce bubbles of oxygen. The more bubbles, the faster photosynthesis is happening.
> ● State three variables that might control the number of bubbles produced.
> ● How would you measure the effects of those variables?

Respiration

Every living cell in a plant needs a supply of glucose for energy. Energy is needed to help the plant grow and to make new substances. The chemical energy stored in the glucose is released by **aerobic respiration**:

$$\text{glucose} \ (C_6H_{12}O_6) + \text{oxygen} \ (O_2) \rightarrow \text{carbon dioxide} \ (CO_2) + \text{water} \ (H_2O)$$

Photosynthesis only happens when there is light but respiration happens *all* the time. During the day, a plant produces more oxygen from photosynthesis than it needs for respiration and so oxygen is given off.

6 a What are the two reactants in aerobic respiration?
  b Why do plant cells need to respire?

7 Graph B shows the levels of oxygen and carbon dioxide in the water around a pondweed plant. Ⓗ Ⓢ Ⓦ
  a Which letter (A–D) do you think represents 23:00 hrs?
  b Which line shows the oxygen concentration, X or Y?
  c Explain why line X goes up between letters B and D.

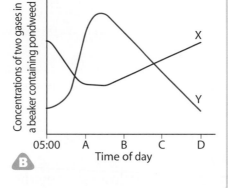

Ⓑ

Glucose is dissolved in water and carried around a plant in **phloem vessels** (made from chains of living phloem cells). Root cells get glucose from the phloem vessels. They also need oxygen, which they get from the soil. If soil becomes flooded or waterlogged, roots cannot get enough oxygen to respire and so the plant can die.

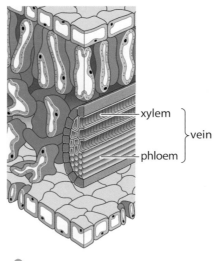

Ⓒ *The inside of a leaf showing the **vein**.*

— xylem
⎫
⎬vein
⎭
— phloem

Ⓓ

Swamp cypresses are adapted to their habitat by having special roots that poke up above the water to get air.

I CAN...

o explain why plants need to photosynthesise and respire.
o describe where the raw materials for these processes come from.
o write word equations for these processes. Ⓗ Ⓢ Ⓦ

8 Why is flooding of fields a problem for farmers growing crops?

How do plants get what they need for photosynthesis?

Getting water

Roots are **adapted** to their **function** by being branched and spread out, helping them to get water from a large volume of the soil. They also have specialised **root hair cells** that give them a large surface area so they can **absorb** water quickly.

> **!** A rye grass plant can grow roots with a total length of over 600 km in about four months.

1 **a** What do root hair cells do?
   b How are they adapted to their function?

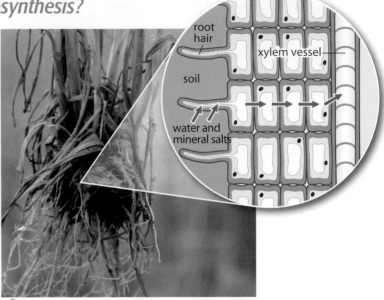

A *Many root hair cells form root hair **tissue**, which covers roots.*

Water passes through other cells in the root until it reaches **xylem vessels** (pronounced '*zy-lem*'). These long tubes are formed when chains of xylem cells become hollow, as they die. The tubes carry water to the leaves.

Water is needed for photosynthesis, to keep leaves cool, and to fill up cells to help them expand and keep them firm. If there is too little water, the cells sag and the plant droops – it **wilts**.

2 How are xylem cells adapted to their function?
3 Celery stems contain a lot of xylem vessels. What could you do to show that they carry water? Ⓗ Ⓢ Ⓦ
4 **a** Give two examples of tissues from this page.
   b Give two examples of **organs** from this page.
5 List three reasons why plants need water.

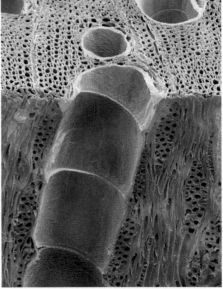

B *Xylem vessels at a magnification of ×110.*

Getting mineral salts

Water from the soil contains dissolved **mineral salts**. These are needed for a plant to stay healthy. For example, without potassium salts a plant cannot photosynthesise, and **nitrates** are needed to make proteins.

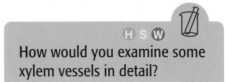

Ⓗ Ⓢ Ⓦ
How would you examine some xylem vessels in detail?

Plants that live in soils without many mineral salts may get them from insects! Venus flytraps have specialised cells that form 'trigger hairs'. If an insect touches a hair more than once, a signal is sent to cells in the 'hinge'. These cells change shape and the trap shuts. Enzymes then slowly digest the insect.

trigger hair

hinge

C

> **6** Why do you think a Venus flytrap hair needs to be touched more than once? (*Hint:* think about when it rains.)

Getting carbon dioxide

Stomata are small holes in a leaf that are opened and closed by **guard cells**. When they are open, usually when there is light, carbon dioxide can enter the leaf by **diffusion**. Leaves are thin, so the carbon dioxide does not have to diffuse very far into a leaf before getting to cells. Plants also lose water and oxygen through stomata.

Getting light

Palisade cells are adapted to their function by containing lots of **chloroplasts** (where photosynthesis occurs). The chloroplasts move nearer to the surface of the leaf in dim light. They move in the opposite direction in bright light to stop them being damaged.

cuticle
upper epidermis
chloroplast
palisade cell
xylem vessels carry water
phloem vessels carry food
vein
lower epidermis
spongy cells
carbon dioxide
cuticle
oxygen
guard cell
stoma
water vapour

D *The inside of a leaf.*

E *A stoma at a magnification of ×430.*

> **7** What are cells that open and close stomata called?
> **8** What process causes particles to move from where there are lots of them to where there are fewer?
> **9 a** In which cells, in diagram D, will no photosynthesis occur? **H S W**
> **b** List the other cells in order of amount of photosynthesis. Start with those in which most photosynthesis occurs.
> **10** Why do you think stomata shut at night?

I CAN...

- describe how water and carbon dioxide get to leaves.
- explain how plant organs and cells are adapted to their functions.
- explain why water is needed by plants.

How do farmers make sure their crops grow well?

All the material in an organism is its **biomass**, which is made of thousands of different substances. Most of these substances are made using glucose.

1 In plants, what are the following used for?
a cellulose b fats
c proteins

aerobic respiration (for energy)

glucose molecules (made of oxygen, carbon and hydrogen)

mineral salts from the soil (e.g. nitrates)

amino acids

proteins are made from amino acids

proteins – used for growth and repair and stored in some seeds

starch – used as an energy store

cellulose – used in cell walls

fats – used in cell membranes and as energy stores

A

The glucose made in photosynthesis is quickly turned into **starch** to be stored. The starch can then be broken down again into glucose and other sugars, which travel in phloem vessels to where they are needed.

2 Look back at van Helmont's experiment on page 32. Explain why you think his soil lost a small amount of mass.

How would you find out where starch is stored in plants?

Crops are grown for food and to make things like biofuels, paper, textiles and some plastics. Whatever the crop, the farmer wants to get it to produce as much useful biomass (**yield**) as possible, and as cheaply as possible.

Since the 1930s, 200 000 km of the UK's hedges have been removed. In 1997 it became law for people to get permission to remove hedges.

Machinery

Forests are cut down to make new farmland and hedgerows are removed to create more space for big machines to get around. Machines can plant and harvest crops faster than humans.

Pesticides

Pesticides kill **pests** – organisms that damage crops. **Insecticides** kill insect pests. **Fungicides** kill fungi that cause diseases that stop plants photosynthesising so well.

3 Why do farmers want to harvest ripe crops quickly?
4 Suggest reasons why a farmer might decide: **H** **S** **W**
   a to remove a hedge
   b not to remove a hedge.

wheat sprayed with selective herbicide

unsprayed wheat

B

Herbicides (**weedkillers**) kill weeds, which would otherwise **compete** with the crop plants for water, light and mineral salts. Modern herbicides are **selective**. This means that they can kill plants with broad leaves (like many weeds) but do not affect crop plants with narrow leaves (like wheat).

5 a Why would a farmer use a selective herbicide? Ⓗ Ⓢ Ⓦ
  b Why might a poor farmer in Africa not use a selective herbicide?

Plant varieties

Scientists create new **varieties** of plants. Some of these have a greater yield than others.

wheat variety grown today

wheat variety grown in the 1950s

C

6 a What differences are there between the two varieties of wheat? Ⓗ Ⓢ Ⓦ
  b Suggest two reasons why the old variety of wheat is no longer grown.

Fertilisers

Fertilisers contain mineral salts. Many farms use both artificial fertilisers and natural fertilisers like manure (animal waste). **Organic farms** only use natural fertilisers. Microbes and other small organisms, called **decomposers**, break down manure and release the mineral salts from it.

Ⓗ Ⓢ Ⓦ
Justus von Liebig (1803–1873) developed the first artificial fertiliser in 1840.

plants with fertiliser

plants without fertiliser

D

7 Farms in the UK today produce 35% more food per m² than they did in 1973. Explain why. Ⓗ Ⓢ Ⓦ

I CAN...

o describe how farmers use scientific advances to produce as much biomass as possible. Ⓗ Ⓢ Ⓦ

Greenhouses

Greenhouses can be used to make sure that plants have the best conditions for growth – the amount of warmth, light and water given to plants can all be carefully controlled.

How can plants be grown without soil?

HowScienceWorks

Mineral salts are compounds that contain a metal and a 'salt group', like nitrate or phosphate. Without these, plants can suffer from deficiency diseases. Plants use nitrates to make proteins; too little results in poor growth. Phosphates help to make cell membranes and allow healthy root growth. Potassium is needed for the enzymes in respiration and photosynthesis. A lack of salts containing potassium causes leaves to turn yellow.

In 1699 an English scientist called John Woodward (1665–1728) gave a lecture to the Royal Society, explaining how he had grown spearmint plants without soil. He found that the plants grew better in impure water than in pure water.

In the 1930s, American scientists Dennis Hoagland and Daniel Arnon published a paper in a scientific journal explaining the best combinations and amounts of mineral salts to dissolve in water for different plants. These solutions are still used today.

Growing plants without soil is called **hydroponics**. The lettuces in photo B are being grown in tubes through which water is flowing. The water contains mineral salts and lots of dissolved oxygen.

1 For each of the plants in diagram A write down:
   a which mineral salt is lacking.
   b what this mineral salt is used for.

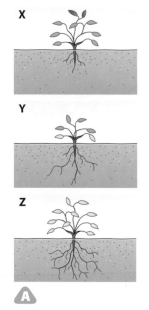

X

Y

Z

A

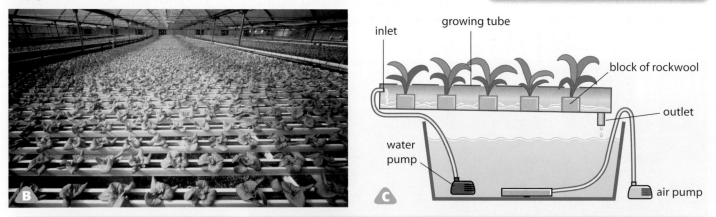

B

inlet

growing tube

block of rockwool

outlet

water pump

air pump

C

2 Explain John Woodward's observation.

3 Explain why the water in the tubes in diagram C has to have oxygen added to it.

4 A lot of minerals in the soil come from humus (rotting dead plants) which also holds the soil together. Suggest why hydroponics is used in the desert regions of Israel.

5 Suggest some advantages and disadvantages of hydroponics.

How do farmers use plant hormones?

How**S**cience**W**orks

A **hormone** is a chemical made by some cells in an organism to change how other cells work. Human hormones include insulin (which controls blood glucose levels).

Auxins are **plant hormones** that cause cells to get bigger. They are used in rooting powders to make plant cuttings grow roots. Some auxins cause plants with broad leaves to grow out of control and die but have little effect on plants with narrow leaves, like grasses.

Gibberellins are hormones produced by plant embryos inside seeds. They make fruits grow big. Most seedless grapes are naturally very small and so farmers spray them with gibberellins.

A This rooting powder contains auxins.

B

Ethylene is a hormone that is a gas. It is produced by fruits and makes them ripen. Bananas are picked when they are green and are shipped to the UK. They are then put into rooms containing ethylene, to make them ripen and turn yellow.

!

Cut flowers produce ethylene, which makes them die faster. Adding aspirin to their water stops ethylene being produced so that the flowers last longer. Flowers are often sold with a sachet of a chemical that does the same thing.

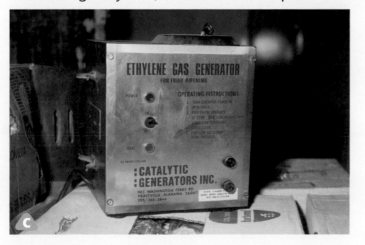

C

1 What would happen if bananas were picked ripe before being transported to the UK?
2 Suggest two ways in which plant hormones could be transported around a plant.
3 Why are seedless grapes sprayed with gibberellins?
4 a What is a selective herbicide?
   b How do some auxins act as selective herbicides?
5 In Central America bunches of bananas that are to be sold locally are wrapped in plastic while still on the plants. Suggest why this is done.

What problems does farming cause?

Farming can damage **habitats** in many ways. Too much fertiliser can get into streams and rivers and cause water organisms to die.

Some insecticides kill helpful insects that eat pests or pollinate plants. A few insecticides stay in the environment for a long time (they are **persistent**) and can poison other animals. Some farmers use **biological control** where they introduce a **predator** to eat the pests. However, the predator can end up becoming a pest!

Selective herbicides may only kill plants that have broad leaves so a crop, like wheat, is not affected. However, many plants in hedges have broad leaves and they are killed.

1 This **food web** is from a hedge next to a wheat field. What would happen if a farmer sprayed his crop with: Ⓗ Ⓢ Ⓦ
   a a general insecticide   b a selective herbicide?

A Fertilisers have caused the fish to die.

B blackbird   owl   dormouse   caterpillar   wheat plant   hazel tree

Genetically modified (GM) plants have been artificially altered to do something (e.g. produce more fruit). Some farmers want to grow them but others think that the plants may damage the environment.

Land may be cleared of trees and hedgerows to make space for crops or machinery. This destroys the habitats of animals and so their **populations** fall.

In some parts of the world huge areas of rainforest have been cut down in order to grow crops.

2 A scientist wants to genetically modify an apple tree. Suggest five **characteristics** that this tree should have. Ⓗ Ⓢ Ⓦ

! Worldwide, 12 hectares (the area of a British village) of trees are cut down every minute.

C

Scientists do not always agree on how damage affects animals. For example, some blame hedge removal for the 62% drop in turtle dove numbers since 1972. Others think that droughts in Africa (where the birds spend the winter) are the major cause.

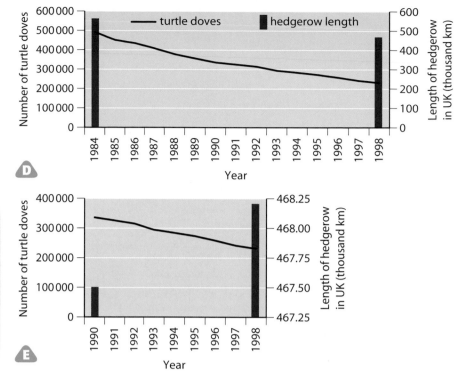

D

E

3 a What conclusions would you draw from each graph – D and E? Ⓗ Ⓢ Ⓦ

b How has the data in the graphs been manipulated so that you draw different conclusions?

Plants remove carbon dioxide from the atmosphere when they photosynthesise. Carbon is 'stored' in trees but the carbon in crops is soon released back into the atmosphere, when the crops are used for food or fuel. Due to the destruction of forests and burning fossil fuels, the amount of carbon dioxide in the atmosphere has been increasing for the last 200 years. Extra carbon dioxide is causing the Earth and its atmosphere to get hotter (**global warming**). The **carbon cycle** shows the processes by which carbon dioxide is removed and released.

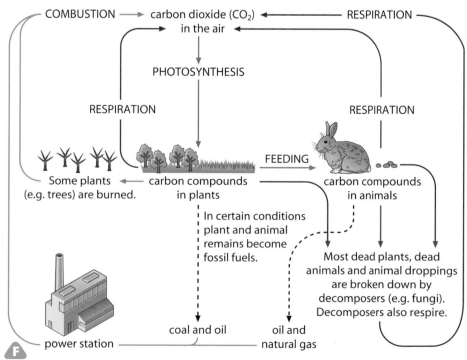

F

4 a List three ways in which carbon dioxide is added to the atmosphere. Ⓗ Ⓢ Ⓦ

b Which of these has increased in the last 200 years?

5 Farming can affect many different parts of the carbon cycle. Identify as many of these as you can. Ⓗ Ⓢ Ⓦ

6 Draw a table to show the advantages and disadvantages of: **a** clearing land **b** insecticides **c** herbicides **d** fertilisers. Ⓗ Ⓢ Ⓦ

I CAN...

o use models (e.g. food webs, carbon cycle) to explain changes in the environment. Ⓗ Ⓢ Ⓦ

o evaluate the advantages and disadvantages of different farming methods. Ⓗ Ⓢ Ⓦ

HowScienceWorks

Should we farm organically?

Organic food is grown without artificial fertilisers and without many pesticides. Some people think that we should make all farming in the UK organic.

> Organic food is expensive to produce. Organic food costs up to 30% more than other food. If we made all farming organic, many people would not be able to afford food.

A *Prof. Tony Trewavas, plant scientist.*

> 31000 tonnes of pesticides are applied to UK farmland each year. In total, organic farms only use about 10 tonnes. Many scientists think that pesticides are bad for you.

B *Sam Allen, of the Soil Association, which sets the rules for organic farming in the UK.*

> The amount of wheat that the world produces has quadrupled in the last 50 years. It will have to go up about the same amount again in order to feed the world. We either clear rainforests to grow it or we use chemicals to get as much out of our farmland as possible. We will protect the wild environment by making better use of farms.

C *Prof. Bill McKelvey, head of the Scottish Agricultural College.*

> In our study of 180 farms over five years, we found that organic farms contained over 80% more plant species, 33% more bats, 17% more spiders and 5% more birds.

D *Dr Lisa Norton, of the Centre for Ecology & Hydrology.*

1 a What percentage of the total amount of pesticides used in the UK do organic farms use?

b Which figure (the number of tonnes or the percentage) do you think organic supporters use when backing up their arguments for organic farming?

c Why do you think this?

2 a What sort of fertiliser will organic farms use?

b Explain how plants get mineral salts from this fertiliser.

3 Do you think that organic farming is more **sustainable** than standard methods of farming using chemicals? Explain your answer.

HAVE YOUR SAY

Do you think that we should make all UK farming organic?

HowScienceWorks

People with different jobs work together at a crime scene to try to answer these questions:
- Who was the victim?
- When did the crime happen?
- Where did the crime happen?
- What happened?
- Who committed the crime?
- Why did they commit the crime?

These are legal questions. **Forensic science** is the use of science to answer legal questions.

Emma Jelbert trains Scenes of Crime Officers (SOCOs). SOCOs collect evidence from crime scenes. Detectives and other experts work with SOCOs to make sure that evidence is collected properly. The police also protect the crime scene to make sure that other people (like the press and the general public) do not enter.

A *Emma Jelbert was a Scenes of Crime Officer. She now trains other SOCOs.*

In cases of an unexplained death a forensic pathologist is called in. This is a doctor who specialises in working out how people died, and can give an opinion in a court.

Sometimes other people are needed. These might include:
- fire experts (to examine how a fire might have started).
- engineers (to do a **risk assessment** to see how safe the site is for the SOCOs).
- other forensic experts (who examine evidence to present in a court case).
- bomb disposal experts (who can make explosive devices safe).

B

1 a List all the jobs on this page.
  b Suggest how a knowledge of science is useful for each job.
2 Suggest three types of evidence that a SOCO might collect.
3 a Look at photo B. How is this crime scene being protected?
  b Why do you think crime scenes need protection?

How can knowledge of plants help a crime investigation?

Patricia Wiltshire is a forensic **botanist** – she studies plants. Her knowledge helps her to suggest what has happened in a crime and explain this to a court.

> 1 Write a definition of 'forensic botanist' for the glossary.

A *Dr Patricia Wiltshire is a forensic botanist.*

In one murder investigation, Patricia noticed new shoots growing from nettle plant stems. She knew that these shoots only grow when the plants have been stepped on and so was able to show police the route that the killer took. She also knew how quickly these shoots grow and told police that the killer was there two weeks before.

Forensic botanists will also identify any leaves found at crime scenes, to work out whether a body has been moved.

> 2 Explain how identifying leaves can be used to work out if a body has been moved. Ⓗ Ⓢ Ⓦ

B *Leaves from different plants have different shapes and sizes.*

Plant lifecycles

Forensic botanists need to know about the **lifecycles** of many plants. Diagram C shows a typical lifecycle of a **flowering plant**.

> 3 Look at diagram C. The flower is an **organ system** that contains male and female **organs**.
> a What two parts make up the male reproductive organ?
> b What is the function of the top part of this organ?
> c What is the female sex cell called?
> d This plant uses **sexual reproduction**. Explain what this means.
> 4 What happens when a seed germinates?

> ❗ In summer there can be up to 3000 pollen grains per cubic metre of air. These large amounts can cause hay fever.

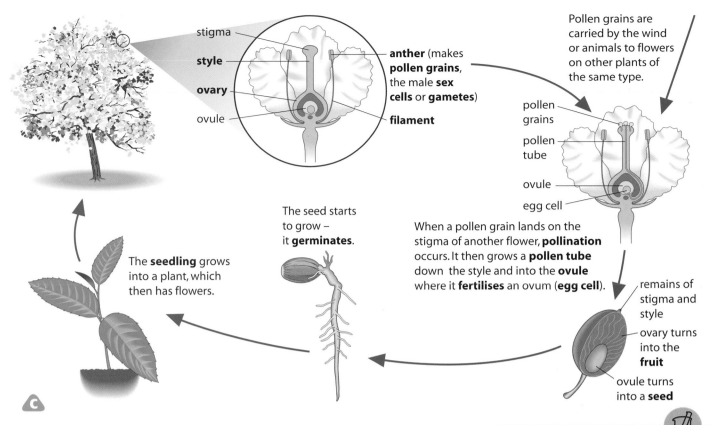

stigma

style

ovary

ovule

anther (makes **pollen grains**, the male **sex cells** or **gametes**)

filament

Pollen grains are carried by the wind or animals to flowers on other plants of the same type.

pollen grains

pollen tube

ovule

egg cell

When a pollen grain lands on the stigma of another flower, **pollination** occurs. It then grows a **pollen tube** down the style and into the **ovule** where it **fertilises** an ovum (**egg cell**).

remains of stigma and style

ovary turns into the **fruit**

ovule turns into a **seed**

The seed starts to grow – it **germinates**.

The **seedling** grows into a plant, which then has flowers.

C

Patricia used pollen to provide more evidence to convict the killer who walked through the plants at the crime scene. She showed that the mixture of types of pollen found at the murder scene matched the mixture found on the murderer's shoes and in his car.

Other parts of a plant's lifecycle are also important to a forensic botanist. Some of the cells in a tree use **cell division** to increase their numbers and allow the tree to grow. Inside the trunk and roots, this growth forms rings – one ring grows each year. Counting the rings of tree roots growing through a buried skeleton allows you to work out the minimum amount of time that the body has been there.

5 Thirty-two skeletons were found in a grave in Magdeburg, Germany in 1994. There were two historical reports that could explain this:
A – anti-Nazi agents killed by the Gestapo in the spring of 1945
B – soldiers killed by the secret police in the summer of 1953.
Scientists found large amounts of lime tree, plantain and rye pollen in the skulls of the skeletons. These plants all flower during the summer.
a Which of the theories is supported by the pollen evidence?
b Explain your reasoning.

6 Photo D shows a healthy root removed from a skeleton.
a What is the minimum time that the body has been buried?
b Why can't you say exactly how long ago the body was buried?

H S W

Forensic botanists need to tell the difference between wind-carried pollen and pollen carried by insects.

o How could you find out about these differences?

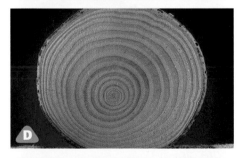

D

I CAN...

o recall the main parts of the lifecycle of a flowering plant.

o recognise how a knowledge of plants can be used in forensics.

H S W

How can knowledge of insects help a crime investigation?

In thirteenth century China, a villager was killed with a rice-harvesting sickle. The investigator lined up the villagers with their sickles. The murderer was identified by flies landing on his sickle, attracted by specks of blood left on it, even though he had wiped it clean.

Scientists who study insects (entomologists) are often asked to help solve crimes.

Time of death

When an animal dies, blowflies are attracted to the body. They lay eggs that hatch into **larvae** ('maggots'). The larvae feed on the body for about a day and then shed their skins to become larger. Diagram B shows the lifecycle.

A *Amoret Whitaker is a forensic entomologist.*

1 **a** What attracted flies to the murderer's sickle?
 b Why is this behaviour useful for flies?
2 Describe Amoret Whitaker's job, without using the words 'forensic' or 'entomologist'. Ⓗ Ⓢ Ⓦ

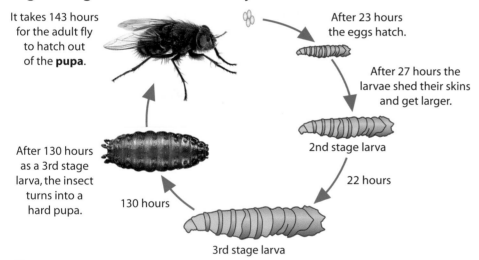

It takes 143 hours for the adult fly to hatch out of the **pupa**.

After 23 hours the eggs hatch.

After 27 hours the larvae shed their skins and get larger.

2nd stage larva

22 hours

After 130 hours as a 3rd stage larva, the insect turns into a hard pupa.

130 hours

3rd stage larva

B *The lifecycle of a blowfly at 20°C (if it is colder, the stages happen more slowly).*

Fly larvae have **innate** (automatic) behaviours that make them move towards or away from some **physical environmental factors** (e.g. light). The way the larvae move (their **response**) helps them find food and so survive. The thing that they move to or away from is the **stimulus**.

How would you investigate how blowfly larvae respond to light and moisture?

3 **a** There are 2nd stage larvae in a body. Estimate the minimum time it has been dead for. Ⓗ Ⓢ Ⓦ
 b What stage larvae would you expect to find if the death occurred 10 days ago?
 c Why does the blowfly stage only tell you the minimum amount of time since death?
4 Why is it important that a forensic entomologist knows how the temperature has changed around a body?

Predators, like carrion beetles, arrive next at a body to feed on blowfly larvae. As the corpse rots, it becomes less attractive to blowflies, and instead attracts insects like cheese skippers. Finally, insects like dermestid beetles feed on the remaining dry tissues (including hair) until only a skeleton is left. Identifying the insects on a body helps a forensic entomologist work out how long it has been in an area.

Dead horse arum flowers smell like rotting meat. This attracts flies to pollinate them.

C

5 Why should a forensic entomologist have a good knowledge of insect **classification**?

6 a Why are carrion beetles only found on a body after blowflies have been there?

b Draw a **food chain** that includes carrion beetles and blowflies.

Social behaviour

Animals that feed on animals that have died are **scavengers**. Crows are scavengers and communicate with each other about where to find food. When a group of crows feeds, some do not eat but look out for danger.

A behaviour in which animals communicate with or react to other animals of the same species is a **social behaviour**.

Bees may build nests in skeletons. Bees also use social behaviour to tell each other where to find food. If a bee finds flowers with lots of nectar, it does a 'waggle dance' back at the nest to tell other bees where to go.

7 Describe two social behaviours of crows and how these help them to survive.

8 Some bees communicate with wasps. Why is this not an example of social behaviour?

9 a How does the waggle dance help bees to survive?

b The waggle dance is an innate behaviour. What does this mean?

bee doing a waggle dance

D

I CAN...

o describe how social behaviours help animals to survive.

o recognise how a knowledge of insects can be used in forensics.

H S W

How can animals help crime detection?

A bee's waggle dance is innate behaviour. However, the bees that watch the dance *learn* where the food is and fly off in its direction. This is **learned behaviour**.

Learned behaviour in bees could be useful in crime solving! Scientists have trained bees to recognise the smells of some explosives. First they give the bees the smell of an explosive. Then they give them some sugar solution. The bee drinks the solution using a tube called a **proboscis** ('*prob-oss-sis*'). Soon, the bee sticks out its proboscis when it smells the explosive, expecting to get some sugar solution.

1 What is learned behaviour?
2 Give an example and explain the use of:
   a an innate human behaviour
   b a learned human behaviour.

A *A bee being trained.*

proboscis

B

3 a Suggest some advantages of using bees rather than dogs to sniff for explosives.
   b Suggest some disadvantages of using bees.
   c Why might a good sense of smell be useful for the survival of bees?

Training dogs

Russian scientist Ivan Pavlov (1849–1936) was interested in the digestive enzymes in dog saliva. Most animals produce saliva when they smell or eat food.

Pavlov noticed that his dogs produced saliva when people in white lab coats came near, with or without food. He thought that the dogs had learned to produce saliva when seeing lab coats because they were fed by people wearing lab coats. To test his theory he rang a bell at feeding time. Soon, the dogs produced saliva just on hearing the bell.

4 a Is producing saliva innate or learned?
   b Why is producing saliva useful for survival?
5 a When saliva is produced normally what is the stimulus and what is the response?
   b What was the stimulus and the response in Pavlov's *trained* dogs?

Rewarding animals after they have responded to a stimulus in a certain way is used to train dogs to look for explosives, drugs and dead bodies. Their very sensitive sense of smell makes them extremely useful for these jobs. The dogs are trained using specially developed scents, including 'dead body smell'.

C Sniffer dogs are often used at airports.

6 Describe how you might train a dog to look for dead bodies.

7 Do you think that training animals in this way is a good or a bad idea? Explain your reasoning. **H** **S** **W**

Bird song

Parrots can learn to mimic human words. In one case, a parrot was stolen (with other items) from a house. The owner spotted the burglars and ran after them shouting 'Robbery! Robbery!'. A little later, the thieves' car was stopped for a routine check and the parrot squawked 'Robbery! Robbery!'. The thieves were arrested.

Most birds can make sounds but they learn their particular songs from their parents. They then use their song to attract mates or tell others where their territory is.

This is like humans. Babies cry innately when they are wet, hurt or hungry. Later, they learn to cry to get attention and then they learn to speak a language.

E A parrot playing with a computer.

8 a A baby is crying. Suggest a stimulus and the response.
 b Is the stimulus internal (inside the baby's body) or external (outside it)?
 c Why is it useful for babies to cry?
9 Babies put many things in their mouths. This is an innate behaviour.
 a Suggest what they learn from doing this.
 b Suggest how this learning is useful.

I CAN...

o describe different innate and learned behaviours and the stimuli that cause them.

o describe how innate and learned behaviours are useful to organisms.

How can psychology help detect and reduce crime?

Humans have both innate and learned behaviours. All behaviours need **neurons** (nerve cells) to make them happen. Neurons are specialised cells that carry electrical signals called **impulses**. They are bundled together into nerves, which form part of the **nervous system**.

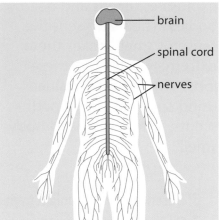

A The nervous system carries impulses all around your body.

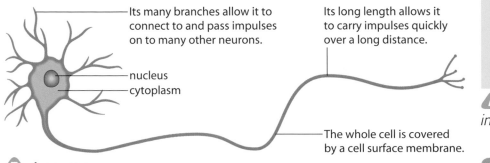

Its many branches allow it to connect to and pass impulses on to many other neurons.

Its long length allows it to carry impulses quickly over a long distance.

nucleus
cytoplasm

The whole cell is covered by a cell surface membrane.

B A neuron.

Innate behaviours

Sneezing and removing your hand quickly from a hot object are innate behaviours. You have little control over them.

Diagram C shows the neurons that automatically make you move your hand away if you touch something hot. Cells in your skin detect the heat and create impulses. These travel along a neuron to your **spinal cord** (a huge bundle of neurons). More impulses are then automatically sent to muscles, which contract to move your hand away.

!
The longest neuron in the body is over 1 m long.

1 List the parts of the nervous system.
2 State two ways in which a neuron is adapted to its function.
3 a Which three parts of a neuron are common to all animal cells?
  b What do these three parts do?

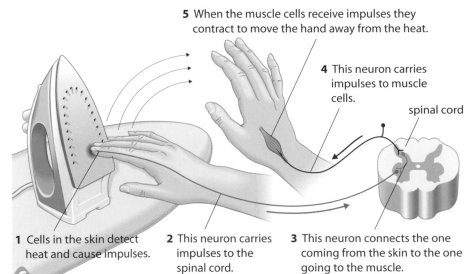

5 When the muscle cells receive impulses they contract to move the hand away from the heat.

4 This neuron carries impulses to muscle cells.

spinal cord

1 Cells in the skin detect heat and cause impulses.

2 This neuron carries impulses to the spinal cord.

3 This neuron connects the one coming from the skin to the one going to the muscle.

4 a Innate behaviours are often quicker than actions that you need to think about. Suggest why.
  b What advantage is there of the behaviour in diagram C being quick?

Learned behaviours

Most of the time you decide what to do using your brain, which is made of billions of neurons connected together. Information about your surroundings is sent from **sense organs** (e.g. eye, ear) to your brain. You use this information to decide what to do. Most of what we do we have had to learn.

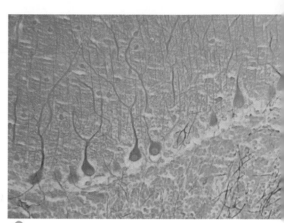

D Neurons in the brain.

> 5 List the three sense organs mentioned on these pages.
> 6 State three of your behaviours that are:
>   **a** innate   **b** learned.

Psychologists at work

Psychology ('*sy-kol-oj-ee*') is the study of human behaviour. Forensic psychology is using psychology to answer legal questions. Some forensic psychologists work on murder cases to try to work out what a murderer is like and how he or she behaves. This may give the police a better idea of who they are looking for.

Forensic psychologists may also help the police interview suspects, witnesses or crime victims. The police need to make sure that the answers to their questions are true. Some forensic psychologists are experts in telling if someone is lying.

> 7 **a** Look at the photos in E. Which is the fake smile? Ⓗ Ⓢ Ⓦ
>   **b** How did you work out your answer?
>   **c** How scientific do you think your answer is?
>   **d** What could you do to be better able to tell fake smiles from real ones?

E

Other psychologists help criminals to change their behaviour. Dr Theresa Gannon is a forensic psychologist who also helps offenders manage their anger. Some people quickly get angry and violent and get into trouble, especially if they have been using alcohol or drugs.

F *Dr Theresa Gannon trains offenders to control their anger.*

> 8 What do you think is the point of Dr Gannon's work? Ⓗ Ⓢ Ⓦ
> 9 Violent behaviour can be triggered by external stimuli and internal stimuli. Suggest one of each type of factor.

I CAN...

- recall the parts and adaptations of neurons.
- recall the parts of the nervous system.
- identify some human behaviours as innate or learned, and explain their uses.
- describe how psychology can be useful. Ⓗ Ⓢ Ⓦ

What are the different sorts of learning?

Psychologists and **ethologists** (scientists who study animal behaviour) have identified different ways in which humans and animals learn.

In **classical conditioning,** a new external stimulus happens at the same time as a stimulus that causes an *innate* response. The new stimulus then also causes the innate response. Pavlov's dogs (page 48) are an example.

A *Pavlov collected the dogs' saliva in a tube.*

Trial and error learning is when animals learn to associate an action with a good or bad event, by trial and error. A rat in a cage might press a lever by accident and get food. It soon learns that pressing the lever will deliver food.

Imprinting is a behaviour learned during a short 'window' of time in an animal's development. For a few hours after hatching, some birds will closely follow the first moving object they see after they hatch.

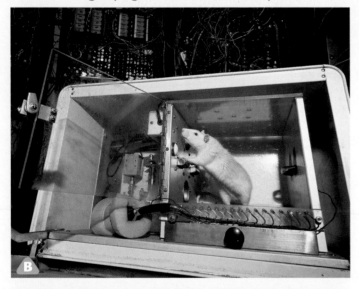

B

C *These young cranes were imprinted onto the hang glider of Angelo d'Arrigo (1961–2006). He taught them how to migrate!*

1 Alcoholism can sometimes be treated by putting a substance into drinks to make the drinker sick.
   a How does this treatment try to stop someone drinking? **H S W**
   b What sort of learning is this an example of?
2 Suggest why imprinting is important for the survival of young ducks.
3 Grizzly bears fish for salmon by leaping at them in the water. Older bears can catch more fish.
   a How is this learning useful to bears?
   b What sort of learning is this an example of?
4 Should experiments like those shown in A, B and C be carried out? Explain your reasoning. **H S W**

How does memory work?

Many experiments have been carried out on animals and humans to try to establish how memory works. Scientists still do not fully understand how it works but they do know that neurons are important.

When you see something, impulses are generated that travel along a whole series of neurons, called a **neuron pathway**. This neuron pathway gradually disappears as your brain gets rid of unused memories.

The more recently a neuron pathway has been used, the easier it is to retrieve that memory. It takes time for unused memories to disappear.

The more a neuron pathway is used the less likely it is to disappear. If you repeat something again and again, you will be able to remember it for a long time.

B *Actors learn lines by repetition.*

Neuron pathways created by uncommon events are also 'stronger'. Some people use this idea to remember things by linking memories to silly rhymes and images.

If you learn the same thing in different ways you will create more neuron pathways to the same memory and so that memory is less likely to disappear.

A *This mouse has remembered how to get through this maze.*

Stephen Wiltshire has an incredible memory for buildings. After a brief helicopter ride along the Thames, he drew this picture from memory.

C

1 What is a neuron pathway?

2 a What did you eat for your last meal?
   b What did you eat for lunch last August the 10th?
   c Explain why one is easier to remember than the other.

3 a Use the information on this page to suggest three methods that could help you to remember things. **H S W**
   b Explain why each of these ways works.

HowScienceWorks

How can a jury be sure someone is guilty?

The evidence against someone accused of a serious crime is heard in a court. The jury (12 ordinary people) listen to barristers. The prosecution barrister tries to convince the jury that the suspect is guilty and the defence barrister does the opposite.

A *A typical courtroom.**

*This photo has been posed by models. It is not of actual people, or meant to be representative of actual people who have been involved in court business or court cases. HMCS

The barristers question the victims, witnesses and suspects. The judge makes sure that these questions are fair, and are not trying to make people say certain things. The jury must decide if the evidence presented by the barristers is:

- valid – relevant to the case.
- accurate – the result of careful, balanced questioning.
- reliable – the answers given by different people are the same.

These 'rules' to judge something are called **criteria**. We use the same criteria in science to judge how good the evidence is that supports or disproves a theory.

1 Why might it be useful for barristers to know about science?

2 a What criteria are used to judge evidence?
  b Explain how you would judge *scientific* evidence using these criteria.
3 There is a crack in a valuable china vase in a museum. There is a theory that someone has dropped it.
  a Use criteria to evaluate each of these pieces of evidence.
    W – Vases can crack if they are dropped.
    X – Derek says he thinks he heard PJ drop a vase.
    Y – A study of 1000 old china vases has found that they are less valuable if cracked.
    Z – Martin, PJ and Lito say that they saw Derek drop the china vase.
  b Which is the best piece of evidence?

HAVE YOUR SAY

Some people think that the evidence in some very complicated trials is too difficult for a jury to understand. They think that these trials should be heard by judges or experts, rather than a jury. What do you think of this idea?

9Ea Building for the future

When architects design buildings they usually choose materials that will look good for a long time. The **properties** of the materials help the architect decide what to use.

Until just over 200 years ago, most large buildings were built of materials such as stone, brick and wood. Stone blocks and bricks make strong weatherproof walls, and wood is strong and flexible to support floors and roofs. Some metals were used for roofing, water pipes and decoration. Modern **concrete** was invented about 300 years ago to replace expensive stone.

A The Parthenon was built of marble 2500 years ago and has survived acid rain, fire and earthquakes.

Today large buildings mostly have steel frames. Steel is stronger than stone so the frame, not the walls, holds the building up and we can build much higher. Many materials can be used as **cladding** for the walls, such as thin stone, glass, metal sheet, bricks, concrete or even plastic. The choice will depend on the effect the architect wants.

B The Reliance Building was built in 1895 in Chicago. It was one of the first large buildings to have a steel frame.

C Modern materials and computer design can create interesting building shapes.

1 Look at photo A.
   a What properties must this stone have?
   b Explain your answer.
2 The invention of steel changed the way we build in our cities.
   a Explain why steel made this possible.
   b List some of the effects that the use of steel has had on cities and the people who live in them. For each effect, say whether it is an advantage or a disadvantage (or both) and explain why.

9Ea A roof over our heads

Why are only some metals used in buildings?

Metal elements form a large part of the periodic table (see page 190). The rest of the elements are grouped as **non-metals** and **semi-metals**. Table A shows some of the properties of metal and non-metal elements. Semi-metals have some properties of both the other groups.

Property	Metals	Non-metals
state at room temperature	usually solids	half are gases
melting and boiling points	often high	often low
conduction of heat and electricity	good	poor (make good insulators)
flexibility	**rigid** when thick, bendy when thin	usually **brittle** – break when bent
malleability	malleable – can be hammered or rolled without cracking	not malleable
ductility	ductile – can be drawn out into wires	not ductile
magnetism	only iron, nickel and cobalt are magnetic	not magnetic
oxides	metal oxides are **bases** (or **alkalis** when dissolved in water)	non-metal oxides are acids

A

1 Are the following statements about elements true or false? If they are false, explain why.
   a All metals are magnetic.
   b All metals are good conductors.
   c All non-metals are solids.
   d All metals are solids.
   e All metals have high melting points.
   f When sulphur burns, it forms an alkaline gas.

2 Pencil 'lead' is made from graphite. Graphite is soft and conducts electricity. It is very difficult to melt. Pencil leads break quite easily. Graphite can burn to give carbon dioxide, which is slightly acidic.
   Explain, with reasons, whether you think graphite is a metal or non-metal. **H S W**

There are also differences between the properties of different metals. Their properties affect how they are used in buildings.

B *The walls of the Guggenheim Museum in Bilbao are clad with sheets of titanium.*

3 Look at photo B. Which properties make titanium a useful building material?
4 The metals in the first two columns of the periodic table react easily with other elements. Suggest why they are not useful building materials.

Many of the metals used for buildings react slowly with chemicals in the air. For example, titanium reacts with oxygen.

titanium + oxygen → titanium oxide

Titanium oxide is a similar colour to titanium, so this reaction doesn't change its appearance. Titanium oxide is unreactive with other chemicals in the air, so it won't change any further. Copper, however, reacts with oxygen and other chemicals in the air and slowly turns green.

An architect needs to consider the cost as well as all the properties of a metal, because there will be a limited amount of money to construct the building.

old copper roof
new copper roof

C *All of this roof is copper, but part of it has been replaced with new metal.*

Metal	Strength (MPa)	Density (g/cm³)	Relative cost	Reaction with chemicals in air
copper	224	8.7	££	turns from shiny copper to bright green
gold	130	19.3	£££££	no reaction, stays shiny gold
titanium	230–460	4.5	£££	forms oxide layer, similar colour to metal
zinc	110–150	7.1	£	forms oxide layer, paler grey than metal

MPa = megapascal. 1 MPa = 100 000 N/m²

D *Comparison of metals used for roofs.*

5 Look at table D.
  a Give one property that makes titanium useful for cladding walls.
  b Give two reasons why an architect might choose copper rather than zinc for a roof.
  c Explain why an architect needs more data than are shown in table D to make a choice. **H S W**

6 Explain why gold is rarely used on roofs. Give as many reasons as you can.

E *These roofs are covered in a thin layer of gold.*

I CAN...

o describe some properties of metal and non-metal elements.
o explain how decisions can be reached about which metals to use when building. **H S W**

What happens when acids and metal oxides react?

The oxide layer that forms on titanium and some other metals protects the metal from damage by water and air. However, that protection can be damaged by **acid rain**.

Metal oxides are bases and they react with acids to form **salts** and water. For example, when copper oxide is added to sulphuric acid, there is a reaction and copper sulphate is produced. Copper sulphate is a special type of **compound** that we call a salt.

How would you investigate what happens to the pH of hydrochloric acid when copper oxide is added?

A

sulphuric acid	+	copper oxide	→	copper sulphate + water
H_2SO_4	+	CuO	→	$CuSO_4$ + H_2O

blue copper sulphate solution

unreacted black copper oxide

B

This is an example of a **neutralisation reaction**. The acid has a pH of about 2, but the copper sulphate solution at the end of the reaction is pH 7 which is neutral.

The general **word equation** for a neutralisation reaction is

acid + base → salt + water

Neutralisation reactions can also produce salts that are useful in buildings. For example, copper sulphate can protect wood against decay by fungi, and lithium nitrate helps to stop concrete cracking after it has set.

1 Look at the photos in B.
  a How can you tell that a reaction occurred?
  b Why are there no bubbles in the photos?

C *Plasterboard is made from paper strengthened with the salt calcium sulphate.*

2 a Give two examples of salts.
  b For each salt, write down the name of the acid and the metal oxide that could be reacted together to make them. Then write out a word equation for each reaction.
3 If you had made copper sulphate solution, as shown in picture B, describe how you would make copper sulphate crystals from the neutralised solution.

I CAN...

o give the word equation for a neutralisation reaction. H S W
o identify changes that show a reaction has occurred. H S W

How can we make copper sulphate?

Many copper salts are **toxic** to living organisms. About three-quarters of the copper sulphate that is produced is used in pesticides.

> **1** Copper sulphate is very soluble in water. Explain why this property is useful when using it on living organisms.

Rocks that contain useful minerals are called **ores**. Some copper ores contain copper sulphide, which is heated with oxygen to form copper oxide and sulphur dioxide. The copper oxide is reacted with sulphuric acid to form copper sulphate solution.

We can show these reactions as **symbol equations**, using chemical symbols:

$$2CuS + 3O_2 \rightarrow 2CuO + 2SO_2$$

$$H_2SO_4 + CuO \rightarrow CuSO_4 + H_2O$$

> **2** Copper sulphate solution is evaporated to leave copper sulphate crystals. How does the rate of cooling affect crystal size?

Copper sulphate can also be produced from scrap metal. Scrap copper is heated with sulphur to form copper sulphide, which is then turned into copper oxide and reacted with sulphuric acid.

We can also get copper sulphate from ore that contains little copper. Dilute sulphuric acid is drained slowly (leached) through piles of crushed ore. This reaction is very slow but needs no heat.

HowScienceWorks

A Natural building materials can be treated with copper compounds to stop decay.

B A copper ore mine in Tucson, Arizona.

> **3** Write symbol equations for these reactions.
>   **a** sulphuric acid + iron oxide
>   **b** sulphuric acid + magnesium oxide
> **4** Write symbol equations for the formation of:
>   **a** copper sulphide.   **b** iron sulphide.
> **5** Hydroxides (e.g. sodium hydroxide, NaOH) react with acids in a similar way to oxides. Write symbol equations to predict what will happen in these reactions.
>   **a** sodium hydroxide + hydrochloric acid
>   **b** potassium hydroxide + nitric acid (HNO_3)
> **6 a** Draw up and complete a table with the following headings to compare the three methods of making copper sulphate.
>
> | Starting materials | Heat needed? | Disadvantages |
> | --- | --- | --- |
> | | | |
>
>   **b** Explain where each method would be most useful.

How can we make metals more useful?

Very few metals are used in buildings in their pure form. This is because we can change them in ways that make them more useful. We make them into **alloys**, which are **mixtures** of metals, or metals mixed with other materials such as carbon.

Mixing metals changes their properties. Brass is an alloy of copper and zinc. If you compare the strength of brass in table B below with the values for copper and zinc in table D on page 57, you can see that brass is much stronger.

A Brass is an alloy of copper and zinc that keeps its shape even when hit hard.

	Density (g/cm³)	Strength (MPa)
brass	8.45	330–500
aluminium	2.7	50–90
aluminium/copper/magnesium alloy	2.8	420–500

B

1 Explain why brass is a better metal for making doorknockers than copper.
2 Aluminium is a useful metal because it is very light.
   a Why is a light weight a useful property for building materials?
   b Look at table B. Explain why alloying aluminium with copper and magnesium makes it even more useful.

Metals are **elements** and so contain only one kind of atom. Metals are malleable because their atoms line up in layers. When a force is applied to one side of a metal block, the layers can slide over each other, so the block changes shape without breaking. In an alloy, the mix of atoms almost always makes it more difficult for the layers to slide past each other.

! One of the first uses of an aluminium/copper/magnesium alloy was for the engine of the first aeroplane – the Wright brothers' *Wright Flyer 1* in 1903.

particles moved into new positions

 large force

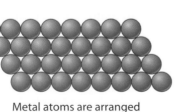

Metal atoms are arranged in layers.

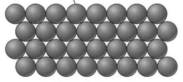

A large force will move the layers.

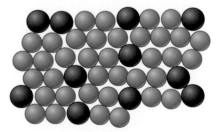

In an alloy, the layers cannot slide as easily.

C A model of the atoms in a metal and an alloy can help explain the differences in their properties.

3 Use diagram C to help you explain why brass is harder than copper or zinc. **H S W**

Iron is one of the most common metals in the Earth's crust, and is easy to extract, so it is cheap. Cast iron is an alloy of iron and carbon. The carbon reduces the melting point and makes the metal flow well. So cast iron is good for making intricate shapes.

Other alloys of iron include steels. Steels contain less carbon than cast iron, but can also contain different amounts of many other different metals. Each steel alloy has different properties depending on what it contains. Mild steel contains very little carbon and is used for constructing building frames. A major problem with mild steel is that the iron in it reacts with oxygen in the air to form **rust**.

iron	+	oxygen	→	iron oxide (rust)
fairly strong				crumbly red
metal				flakes or powder

Stainless steel has chromium and nickel added. The chromium reacts faster than iron with oxygen in the air and forms an unreactive surface layer that protects the rest of the metal.

Metal	Density (g/cm³)	Strength (MPa)	Relative cost
cast iron	7.0–7.4	100–230	1.5
mild steel	7.8	430–490	1
stainless steel	7.8	460–1200	8.1

E

4 Look at table E.
   Explain why the frames of skyscrapers are built with mild steel and not cast iron.

5 Using table E:
   a explain why stainless steel can be used for cladding buildings.
   b explain why stainless steel is not used for building frames.

H S W

When iron is extracted from its ore it is known as pig iron and contains many impurities, including about 4% carbon, which makes it very brittle. English inventor Sir Henry Bessemer (1813–1898) designed a way of making this into steel, by blowing air through it. The oxygen reacted with the impurities forming oxides. It made him a very rich man – over a million pounds, which is about 800 million in today's money.

D These balconies are made from cast iron.

F Stainless steel can be used for cladding buildings.

I CAN...

o describe how alloys make metals more useful.

· o use the particle model to explain why an alloy can be stronger than a pure metal. H S W

Which are the best stones for building?

All the oldest buildings in Britain are made of stone. Stone is very strong under **compression** (squashing forces) but not under **tension** (pulling forces). Stone is heavy, but can also be very resistant to the effects of weather.

A *This slate sign is fixed to the tree by nails. As the tree grew wider, the slate broke.*

1 Look at photo A. The slate was one piece when it was nailed to the tree. Draw a series of sketches with notes to explain how the slate was broken.

2 Look at photo B. Describe the compression forces in the building.

3 Suggest as many reasons as you can why stone was used for important buildings in Britain. ⒽⓈⓌ

The way the rocks were originally formed gives them different properties and this makes them suitable for different building uses. Table C shows this.

B *After the Normans invaded Britain in 1066 they built huge castles and cathedrals to show their power.*

Rock type	How the rocks were formed	Properties	Examples used in building
sedimentary	from layers of **sediment** that were **compacted** and **cemented** together	**porous**, soft, easy to cut in any shape	sandstone limestone
igneous	from magma deep in the Earth or from lava from volcanoes	not porous, very hard	granite
metamorphic	from other types of rock, changed by extreme heat and/or pressure	not porous, very hard	slate marble

C

D *This floor is made of marble.*

4 Explain why marble was used for the floor shown in photo D.

5 Slate splits into thin layers. Give two other reasons why slate is often used for roofs.

6 Suggest why sedimentary rock is used for the walls of buildings.

Porous rocks have tiny holes in them that rainwater can get into. If the water freezes, it expands and breaks the rocks apart. This is an example of **physical weathering**.

Natural rainwater is very slightly acidic, but acid rain is more acidic (pH 5.6 or less). The more acidic the rain, the faster **chemical weathering** of the rocks occurs. The acid reacts with any calcium carbonate in the rock, forming a soluble salt (such as calcium sulphate), which is then washed away.

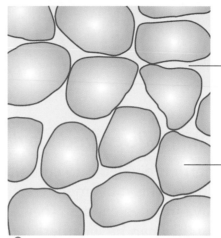

cement – calcium carbonate in limestone; can be iron oxide, calcium carbonate or silica in sandstone

grains – sand (silica) in sandstone or calcium carbonate in limestone

E *Sedimentary stones are made from grains that are cemented together.*

$$\text{calcium carbonate} + \text{sulphuric acid} \rightarrow \text{calcium sulphate} + \text{carbon dioxide} + \text{water}$$

Concrete is an artificial rock that we make cheaply from cement, water and gravel or sand. The properties of the concrete depend on how it is made. So we can make different concretes for different purposes.

H S W

How could you investigate the effect of acid rain on different rocks?

mould for concrete

liquid concrete being poured into mould

F *Concrete is usually delivered as a liquid to a building site. It sets hard in a mould that can be any shape.*

The Romans used an early type of concrete made from volcanic ash, lumps of rock and lime (made by heating limestone). The Pantheon in Rome (built about 1800 years ago) has a vast dome made from Roman concrete.

G

7 Use the information on these pages to put these stones in order of speed of weathering: sandstone, limestone, granite. Explain your answer.

8 Marble is a metamorphic rock formed from limestone. Predict the effect of acid rain on marble. Explain your answer.

9 We make more concrete than any other product. Suggest as many reasons as you can for this.

I CAN...

o link the properties of rocks to their uses. H S W
o describe how weathering affects rocks in buildings.

Why do we build with different rocks in different places?

The surface of the Earth is divided into enormous plates which move very slowly. This movement creates huge forces which can release lava from volcanoes. They can also lift rocks to the surface where they can be weathered. Forces deep underground change the rocks into other types. This means that the rocks of the Earth are continually changing, though usually extremely slowly. We can use the **rock cycle** to model how these processes are linked.

Limestone is a sedimentary rock.

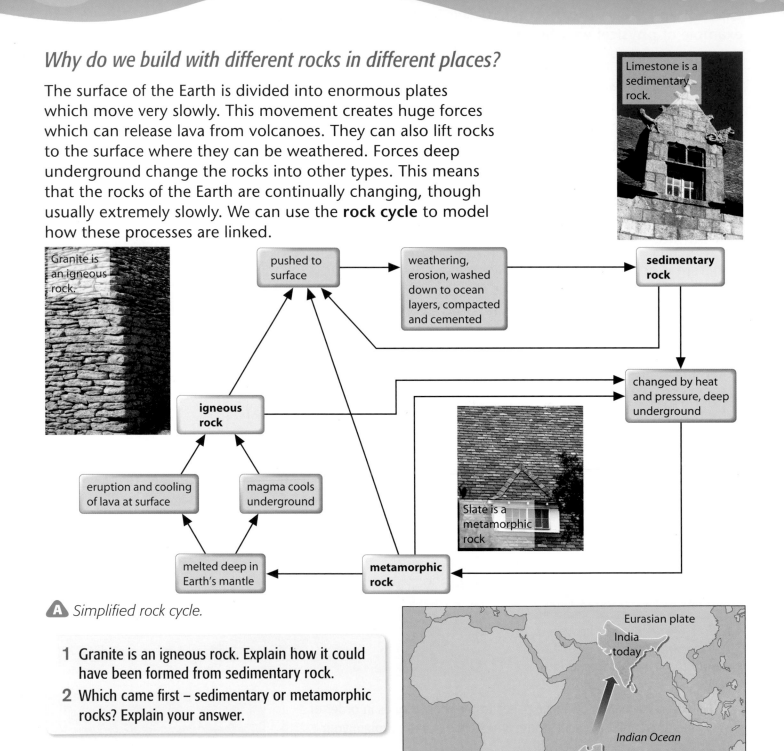

Granite is an igneous rock.

Slate is a metamorphic rock

A *Simplified rock cycle.*

1 Granite is an igneous rock. Explain how it could have been formed from sedimentary rock.
2 Which came first – sedimentary or metamorphic rocks? Explain your answer.

The Himalayas are the highest mountain range on Earth today. They have grown over the last 50 million years as the Indian plate has moved north into the Asian plate, forcing the rocks to twist and rise up.

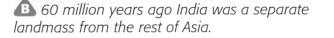

Eurasian plate

India today

Indian Ocean

Indian landmass 60 million years ago

B *60 million years ago India was a separate landmass from the rest of Asia.*

The Himalayas are still rising as India is still moving north. But the mountains are also being affected by weathering. Sediment from the rocks is **eroded** by wind and water, and is washed in rivers down to the ocean where it is building the Ganges Delta. Over 5 cm of sediment is **deposited** each year in some parts of the delta.

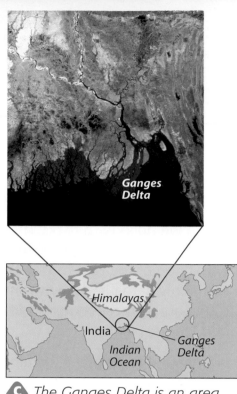

> **3** Suggest which type of rock is probably forming deep below the Himalayas now. Explain your answer.
>
> **4** What needs to happen to the sediments in the Ganges Delta to make them turn into rock?

The **geology** of the British Isles includes rocks of each type. Some of the rocks in Scotland are among the oldest found on the Earth's surface, while those around London are some of the youngest rocks.

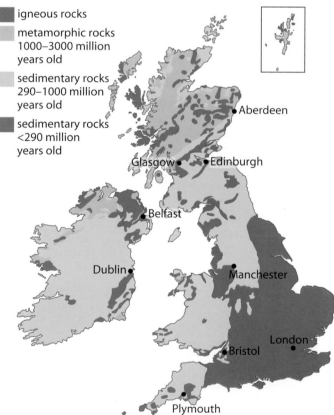

C The Ganges Delta is an area of low-lying land over 350 km wide and is still growing.

Key:
- igneous rocks
- metamorphic rocks 1000–3000 million years old
- sedimentary rocks 290–1000 million years old
- sedimentary rocks <290 million years old

! Over 100 different kinds of marble, imported from 24 different countries, were used to decorate Westminster Cathedral in London.

> **5 a** Look at map D. Which type of rocks are marked as the oldest rocks?
>
> **b** What property of these rocks makes it possible for them to still be here?
>
> **6** Aberdeen is well known for its dark granite buildings, while many buildings in Glasgow are made of red sandstone. Use map D to help you explain this difference. **H S W**
>
> **7** Why would an architect choose to import stone for a new building? Give as many reasons as you can. **H S W**

D Simplified geology of the British Isles (data from the British Geological Survey).

Since rock is so heavy to transport, usually local stone is used for building. However, for the most important buildings, stone may be imported from the best quarries.

I CAN...
- use the rock cycle model to explain how rocks are formed. **H S W**
- explain how the geology of the British Isles has affected the choice of building stone.

A Wood is fairly strong under tension and compression, but it needs protection from water and micro-organisms.

How should we build for the future?

When we build with rocks, metals and concrete we are using **non-renewable resources**. The extraction of the **raw materials** from quarries can badly damage the environment. In addition, transporting these materials to where they are needed uses fuel.

We need to build more **sustainably** for the future. So now architects have to think about the environmental cost of a new building, during its construction and when the building is in use. They can choose to **re-use** materials from old buildings, or use materials that have been **recycled**. Some concrete now uses waste materials from other processes. Alternatively, they can make more use of renewable and local materials.

B Buildings made of mud bricks can be many storeys high and last for hundreds of years, like these in Yemen.

1 List as many ways as you can of how we can build more sustainably. For each way, explain the benefit to the environment.

2 Yemen is a desert area.
  a Suggest why mud bricks are the traditional building material there.
  b How successful do you think mud bricks would be in Britain? Explain your answer.
  c How could you test your answer?

3 If we were to build all buildings in the UK using mud bricks and bags of earth, how would this change the sort of buildings we could construct?

C New ideas for buildings include using earth to make the walls.

HAVE YOUR SAY

Should all new buildings be made from re-used, recycled or renewable resources?

How**S**cience**W**orks

Artists use a variety of different materials for sculptures. Some of these are pure metals, some are mixtures of metals and some are compounds which contain metals.

B This famous statue by Michaelangelo is made of marble (calcium carbonate).

C Willard Wigan makes microscopic sculptures. This sculpture of the football World Cup is made of pure gold and is 2mm high. It took Willard three months to make.

A This tree sculpture is about two metres high and was created in copper by Paul Pearce.

E The sculptor Philip Jackson created the six metre statue of Bobby Moore outside the new Wembley stadium. It is made of bronze (a mixture of copper and tin) and weighs two tonnes.

F Michael Burton created this silver teapot showing a street scene in Martock, Somerset. This is the village where he lives.

D This sculpture is made of sand (mostly silicon dioxide).

1 From the materials shown on this page, name:
  a a metal element.
  b a mixture of metals.
  c a compound that contains a metal.
  d a compound that does not contain a metal.

2 a State four properties of metals.
  b Which property would be most important when making a sculpture? Justify your opinion.

Why do some metals tarnish or corrode?

Tutankhamun's mask is made with pure gold. The mask is over 3000 years old but the gold is still shiny. Gold is **unreactive** – it does not react with the oxygen in the air. Silver is also unreactive but reacts very slowly with oxygen to form a black coating of silver **oxide**. Silver slowly **tarnishes**.

Photo B shows 'Nuclear Energy'. The copper has started to form a black coating of copper oxide. The sculpture in photo C, 'Hill Arches', has reacted further to make copper carbonate ($CuCO_3$), which gives the green colour.

A The burial mask of the Egyptian Pharaoh Tutankhamun, who died in 1322 BCE.

These sculptures by Henry Moore are made of bronze, which is mostly copper.

1 Most of the air is nitrogen and oxygen. Which gas reacts more easily with metals?

2 a Has the copper tarnished in photos B and C? Ⓗ Ⓢ Ⓦ

b What is your evidence? Ⓗ Ⓢ Ⓦ

3 Are each of these substances elements or compounds?

a gold b silver c silver oxide d oxygen

4 Copy and complete these word equations:

a silver + _____ → silver oxide Ⓗ Ⓢ Ⓦ

b copper + oxygen → _____ Ⓗ Ⓢ Ⓦ

5 a What is the name and chemical formula of the green compound in photo C?

b Name the different elements in this compound.

c What *other* gas in the air, apart from oxygen, has reacted with the copper to make this compound?

The sculpture in photo D is mainly iron. The iron has reacted with oxygen from the air – it has **oxidised**. This reaction forms iron oxide (rust), which is a compound of two elements. Iron reacts more quickly than copper. A piece of iron left out in the air will start to go rusty within a few days if it is not protected. Some of the rust then flakes off, leaving more iron exposed to the air. The iron **corrodes** and the sculpture is worn away.

Unreactive metals like silver and gold are found naturally as elements in the environment, because they do not react with air and water. However, they are very expensive to buy because they are very rare. Metals like copper and iron are much more common, but they are found as compounds (usually **ores** containing oxides or sulphides). To get the metal you heat the ore with charcoal (carbon):

iron oxide + carbon → iron + carbon dioxide

E This man is panning for gold in Wanlockhead in Scotland, hoping to find small grains of gold metal mixed in with the mud and stones in the river bed.

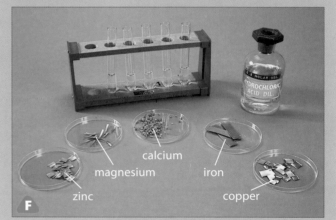

How could you compare the rates at which different metals corrode?

calcium

magnesium   iron

zinc   copper

F

6 Write a word equation for the reaction in which iron rusts.   H S W

7 A metal statue has a mass of 1 tonne. Would the mass be more, less or the same after being outside on display for a year? Explain your answer – you may want to use the words tarnish, oxidise or corrode.

8 Use the evidence on this page to put copper, gold, iron and silver in order to show how quickly they react with air. Explain your reasoning.   H S W

9 How will the different properties of the metals affect the way that sculptors use them?

I CAN...

o explain how metals oxidise, tarnish and corrode.

o write word equations for chemical reactions of metals in air.   H S W

o use evidence to compare how quickly metals react.   H S W

Which metals are the most reactive?

Some metals are much more **reactive** than gold, silver and copper. Calcium is a reactive metal. It reacts with water, giving off hydrogen gas. The resulting solution can then be tested with **universal indicator**.

The word equation for the reaction is:

A *Calcium reacts with water, producing hydrogen gas …*

B *… and an alkaline solution.*

calcium + water → calcium hydroxide + hydrogen

H S W

Calcium reacts with water and the reaction gives off heat. How could you find out what variables will affect the temperature rise?

Imagine a sculpture made of calcium. If it started to rain, you would hear the hiss of the reaction as the drops of water touched the metal. The heat from the reaction could be enough to burn you. Within a few hours, the sculpture would have turned into a white sludge. The element would have become a compound.

That is why we don't find calcium as an element in the environment. Calcium only naturally occurs in chemical compounds like calcium carbonate, which is found in marble statues.

1 Look at photos A and B.   H S W
   a What evidence tells you that a reaction is taking place?
   b What colour does the universal indicator go when it is mixed with the calcium hydroxide solution?
   c What does this tell you about calcium hydroxide?
   d If you held a lighted splint above the tube, what would happen?
2 From the word equation above, write down the names of:
   a two elements.   b two compounds.

E The heat from the reaction of potassium with water is enough to set the potassium on fire.

F A small piece of caesium placed into water reacts so violently that the container explodes.

Sodium and potassium are more reactive than calcium. The heat from the reaction of potassium with water sets the potassium on fire. Caesium is even more reactive.

In general, we can say:

metal + water → metal hydroxide + hydrogen

The sculptures in photo G are made of **salt** (sodium chloride). Reactive metals bond strongly to other elements, and you cannot extract sodium by heating salt with carbon. Instead an electric current is used to split the compound up. First the salt has to be heated to 800 °C – its melting point. Then electrical energy is used to break the bonds between the sodium and the chlorine in the salt. This process is called **electrolysis**. Most reactive metals are produced in this way.

G These sculptures are made of salt (sodium chloride).

H S W

Many reactive metals were discovered about 200 years ago by Sir Humphry Davy (1778–1829) using the new invention of the electrical battery.

3 Write a word equation for the reaction of potassium with water. H S W
4 Look at the periodic table on page 189.
  a On which side do you find the reactive metals?
  b Where do the less reactive metals occur in the periodic table?
5 a Put the three metals caesium, calcium and potassium in order of reactivity. Use the evidence on these two pages to explain your answer. H S W
  b Use this evidence and the periodic table to predict where sodium would come in the series. Explain your reasoning. H S W

I CAN...

o write word equations for the reactions of reactive metals with water. H S W
o describe how reactive metals are extracted from their compounds.
o use evidence to place the reactive metals in order of reactivity. H S W

●●● 71

How can we protect metals against corrosion?

Some metals are corroded by oxygen and water vapour in the air. These metals react even faster with acids. To stop **corrosion**, we can protect the metal.

Rainwater is slightly acidic due to carbon dioxide in the air reacting with the water:

carbon dioxide + water → carbonic acid

If the rainwater is polluted with nitrogen dioxide or sulphur dioxide, the rain becomes more acidic and is known as **acid rain**:

sulphur dioxide + water → sulphuric acid

The sculpture in photo A is protected against attack by paint. Where the paint has started to come off, the iron is exposed. The iron can react with acid rain to make a salt called iron sulphate:

iron + sulphuric acid → iron sulphate + hydrogen

A *A painted iron sculpture near the sea in Alaska, USA.*

What variables affect how quickly magnesium is corroded by acid?

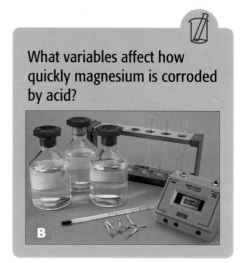

B

1 How does painting a metal stop it from being corroded?
2 a Which gas is given off when metals react with acids?
  b How can we test for this gas?
3 Suggest pH numbers for: a natural rainwater.   b acid rain.
4 Nitric acid is also found in acid rain. Write a word equation for the reaction of iron with nitric acid.

C *This aluminium hand is part of a work called* The Awakening *by J. Seward Johnson Jr.*

Aluminium is quite reactive but does not corrode because it protects itself. A very thin layer of aluminium oxide forms naturally on the surface of the metal. This is insoluble and stops the metal being attacked by air or water.

Photo E shows how quickly aluminium reacts if the protective layer breaks down. Acids also attack this oxide layer and so corrode the metal underneath. For this reason, you should not cook acidic substances like rhubarb in aluminium pans.

E

The *Sir Galahad* burned fiercely when the ship was attacked in the Falklands War in the 1980s. The explosive impact broke the aluminium into small pieces, which then reacted violently with oxygen in the air.

Photo D shows a replica of the Statue of Liberty. It is made of iron but has been coated with zinc. This is called **galvanising**. A thin layer of insoluble zinc carbonate forms and naturally protects the zinc. Even if this layer gets damaged, the iron won't rust straight away, because zinc is more reactive than iron and gets attacked first. This is called **sacrificial protection**. Eventually, after many years, both the iron and zinc get corroded and restoration work has to take place.

Iron may also be **plated** with a less reactive metal such as tin or nickel. However, if the coating is damaged, protection breaks down and the iron may corrode.

5 Suggest two gases in the air that will react with zinc to make zinc carbonate.

6 Write word equations for: (H)(S)(W)
  a aluminium forming its protective layer.
  b zinc reacting with sulphuric acid.

7 Galvanising provides better protection for iron than painting. Why?

8 Sacrificial protection takes place when a magnesium block is attached to the steel on oil rigs. Which metal is 'sacrificed' and which is protected? Explain your answer.

9 Food cans are usually steel coated with either plastic or tin. Explain why it might be unsafe to eat food from a dented tin. (H)(S)(W)

F *This sculpture is made from steel coat hangers plated with nickel.*

I CAN...

o describe ways in which metals can be protected against corrosion and suggest some practical uses of this. (H)(S)(W)

How do we put metals into a reactivity series?

The World Cup Trophy is made of solid, 18-carat (75% pure) gold. It is less than 40 cm high, but has a mass of over 6 kg. The winners of each competition receive a gold-plated replica of this trophy.

1 a Is the **density** of gold high or low?
  b How can you tell from the data given?
2 Explain why the replica trophy would be less valuable than the original.
3 Calculate the 'carat rating' of 100% pure gold. Show your working.

H S W

A

In the group stages of a competition, teams are ranked on points for matches won and drawn. Teams that are equal on points are put in order of goal difference.

The **reactivity series** is a type of chemical 'league table' using criteria that scientists agree about. It shows the metals in order, with the most reactive at the top. To decide where a metal comes in the table, we need to look at whether it reacts with oxygen, water and acids. If metals come out equal on this ranking, we would need to look at how fast they react. Table C on page 75 shows the reactions of some of the metals that you have studied so far.

SPORT MAIL

Position	Team	Played	Goal difference	Points
13	Middlesbrough	8	–7	9
14	Wigan	8	2	8
15	Bolton	8	–2	8
16	Everton	8	–6	8

B

4 Using the reactivity series shown by table C, give the name(s) of:
  a two metals that are more reactive than calcium.
  b the least reactive metal.
  c two metals that are more reactive than lead and less reactive than aluminium.
  d two metals that react with acids but not with water.

! The original World Cup Trophy was first awarded in 1930, and was made of silver plated with gold. It was stolen in London in 1966. A week later, a dog called Pickles found it wrapped in newspaper at the bottom of a garden in south London. It was stolen again in Brazil in 1983 and has not been seen since.

Metal	Reaction with oxygen/air	Reaction with water	Reaction with dilute acids	Cost of metal
Potassium	flammable	flammable	explosive	££
Sodium	flammable	✓✓	explosive	£
Calcium	flammable	✓	✓✓	££
Magnesium	flammable	?	✓	££
Aluminium	✓	✗	✓	££
Zinc	✓	✗	✓	£
Iron	✓	✗	✓?	£
Lead	✓?	✗	?	£
Copper	✓?	✗	✗	££
Silver	?	✗	✗	£££
Gold	✗	✗	✗	£££

Key = flammable   = explosive

✓ = reaction   ✓✓ = fast reaction   ✗ = no reaction   ? = slow or partial reaction

C £ = relatively cheap   ££ = mid price   £££ = expensive

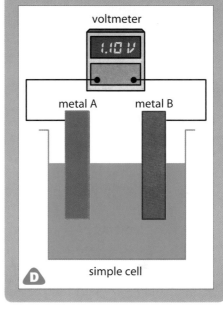

If you put two different metals into an electrical circuit like the one below, a current will flow and you can measure a **voltage**. The voltage depends on the difference between the reactivities of the two metals. How can this provide more evidence for the order of metals in the reactivity series?

voltmeter

1.10 V

metal A   metal B

D   simple cell

5 Use the reactivity series to decide which three of these pairs of substances will react. Write down 'reaction' or 'no reaction' in each case. **H S W**
   a gold + dilute sulphuric acid   b copper + oxygen   c zinc + water
   d sodium + water   e magnesium + hydrochloric acid

6 For the three pairs of substances in question **5** that do react, copy and complete the word equations. (*Hint:* You may need to look back to previous pages in the unit for help.) **H S W**

7 Cobalt can be produced by heating cobalt oxide with either carbon or aluminium. It does not react with water, and only reacts with oxygen at very high temperatures. Cobalt reacts slowly with acids giving off hydrogen. Use this evidence to suggest where cobalt should be placed in the reactivity series.

8 Using all the information in table C, explain why some metals are used for large-scale sculptures while others are not. **H S W**

I CAN...

o describe and compare the reactivity of different metals.
o use a table to interpret data. **H S W**

How can we use the reactivity series?

In sport, we can use a league table to predict the results of future matches. In science, we can use the reactivity series to predict whether chemical reactions will take place. The metals at the top of the table will 'beat' the metals lower down. Unlike a sports league, the predictions are very reliable – you don't get 'shock' results!

Aluminium is more reactive than iron. It reacts with iron oxide like this:

aluminium + iron oxide → aluminium oxide + iron

This is a **displacement reaction**. The aluminium has **displaced** the iron.

A *You can think of aluminium 'pulling' the oxygen away from the iron.*

1 From the word equation above, write down the names of:
  a two elements. **b** two compounds.
2 Using the reactivity series on page 75 (table C), suggest the name of a metal that:
  a could be used instead of aluminium to displace iron from iron oxide.
  b would not displace the oxygen from iron oxide.

Photo B shows a displacement reaction being used to join two sections of steel rail. Iron oxide is mixed with aluminium powder and heated to start the reaction. Aluminium **bonds** more strongly with the oxygen and leaves the iron as a free metal. The reaction produces enough heat to melt the iron, which runs into the gap in the rail. As it cools, it solidifies and welds the sections of rail together.

3 Where does the energy needed to melt the iron come from?
4 Iron oxide melts at 1565 °C. Suggest a value for the melting point of aluminium oxide. Explain your reasoning. Ⓗ Ⓢ Ⓦ

B *The 'thermit reaction' produces molten iron.*

Displacement reactions can also take place in solution. For example, when an iron nail is dipped into copper sulphate solution, a coating of copper forms on the surface of the iron. Some of the iron goes into the solution to form iron sulphate.

Copper, lead and iron have been known since ancient times. They are not very reactive and it is possible to break their bonds with other elements using fire, wood and charcoal. In these reactions, carbon displaces the metals from their compounds.

How can we use the reactivity series to predict whether a metal will react with a solution of a compound?
o What might you measure or observe?

D Copper is easy to extract from its ores, like this lump of 'chalcopyrite'.

Carbon cannot displace reactive metals, like aluminium, from their compounds. Metals like this are extracted from their compounds by electrolysis, and a large amount of electrical energy is used.

5 a Look at photo C. What evidence shows that a reaction has taken place? **H S W**
  b Write a word equation for this reaction. **H S W**
  c Explain why this is a displacement reaction.
  d Use the reactivity series on page 75 to explain why you would expect iron to react with copper sulphate. **H S W**

6 Use the reactivity series on page 75 to predict whether a displacement reaction will occur in each case. Either complete the word equation or write 'no reaction'. **H S W**
  a magnesium + iron chloride →
  b magnesium + potassium sulphate →
  c iron + calcium oxide →
  d zinc + copper nitrate →
  e copper + silver nitrate →

7 Although carbon is not a metal, it can be placed in the reactivity series. Using information from across the whole unit, suggest where you would place carbon in the series, explaining the evidence you have used. **H S W**

! In the 1500s Spanish copper mines used scrap iron to extract copper, a practice that survives to this day.

HowScienceWorks

Why are materials chosen for a particular job?

The Angel of the North, on Tyneside, is one of Britain's most dramatic sculptures. It was finished in 1998, weighs 200 tonnes and is 20 metres high – the height of four double-decker buses. The 54 metre wingspan is almost the same as a Jumbo jet. The total cost was £800,000.

The statue is made of a special type of weathering steel known as Cor-ten. This is mostly iron, mixed with small amounts of copper. The metal reacts with air to form a rusty looking layer on its surface. This layer provides natural protection, which means that the metal does not need to be painted.

> The Angel of the North has become a symbol, which is now recognised throughout the world. It signifies the regeneration of Gateshead and has inspired local people, as well as attracting thousands of people to the area.

A Councillor John McElroy, Gateshead Council.

B

1 Suggest the names of two compounds that might be present in the coating on the metal surface.

2 a If the sculpture had been made of stainless steel, state one way in which it would have been different from the actual statue.
  b How would it have been similar?

3 Explain why the choice of Cor-ten steel for the sculpture might be better than:
  a normal steel. b painted steel. c pure copper.

HAVE YOUR SAY

Is it a waste of money to spend a large amount of money on a statue in an area that suffered job losses, or is it a good way of bringing hope to the area by attracting tourists and media attention?

How**S**cience**W**orks

Pollution happens when substances are added to the environment and cause harm. Air pollution has been a problem since humans started burning fuels. Water pollution has been a problem since people started building villages and towns near rivers, and dumping rubbish and sewage into the water.

'Smog' is produced when water droplets collect around smoke particles from burning coal. The Clean Air Act was passed in the UK in 1956, which helped to control this kind of pollution. Before this, a bad smog could lead to thousands of deaths. Smogs of a different kind still occur in our modern cities, caused by nitrogen oxide gases from car engines.

Smoke can also be a problem indoors. In some countries people burn dried animal dung or wood for cooking or heating their homes. The stoves that they use produce lots of smoke. The smoke can cause breathing problems and can lead to diseases.

A *A London smog in October 1938, at 3.30 in the afternoon.*

B *A London smog in 2008.*

C *Tom Woollard monitors pollution.*

1 a What are the main gases in the air?
  b Which of these gases do our bodies need?
  c How does this gas get into our cells?

2 Which gas (or gases) do plants need?

3 Some of the water we use at home has been taken from rivers.
  a What kinds of pollution might be in this water?
  b How is the water cleaned before it gets pumped to our taps?

4 a Write down as many sources of pollution as you can.
  b Suggest what could be done to control some of this pollution.

D *A house in Mexico.*

What are the causes and effects of natural pollution?

Natural pollutants are substances that occur naturally and are usually present in the environment in small enough quantities that they do not cause any problems. They are called **pollutants** when there is enough of them to cause harm.

When the Earth first formed, about 4600 million years ago, the atmosphere was mainly **carbon dioxide**, produced by volcanoes. About 3500 million years ago micro-organisms that could photosynthesise started to grow on Earth. Their photosynthesis used up carbon dioxide and released oxygen as a waste product. The oxygen was poisonous to other organisms living at the time.

Carbon dioxide in the air dissolves in rainwater and makes it slightly acidic. The **pH** of natural rainwater is between 5.6 and 5.9, but it can be made more acidic by some naturally produced soluble gases. The most important of these gases is carbon dioxide, which is produced by **respiration** in living things, by volcanoes and by **combustion**. Other gases that make rain more acidic are **sulphur dioxide**, produced by volcanoes, and **nitrogen oxides**, formed when lightning makes nitrogen and oxygen in the air react together.

A These mounds are caused by groups of micro-organisms clumping together to form sticky mats. Fossils of similar mounds have been found in rocks 3500 million years old. Scientists think that the first photosynthesising organisms were like these.

B This man is a car park attendant at the Volcano Masaya National Park in Nicaragua. He has to wear a gas mask to protect him from the sulphur dioxide produced by the volcano.

1 Explain why oxygen was a pollutant 3800 million years ago.
2 a Name three soluble gases that can lower the pH of rainwater.
  b What are the natural sources of these gases?
3 Why is carbon dioxide important to life?

The soils on volcanoes are usually very fertile (full of nutrients). However, after an eruption the rainwater is more acidic than normal, and this can make farming more difficult.

How could you find out if acidic rain affects the germination of seeds?

C *Plants damaged by acidic rain from a volcano.*

There are volcanoes erupting somewhere on the Earth all the time, but usually they only affect the area immediately around them. Occasionally a large eruption affects the climate and living things all around the world.

In April 1815 Mount Tambora, in Indonesia, erupted. This was the biggest volcanic eruption for over 1000 years, and it put huge quantities of dust and sulphur dioxide into the atmosphere. Winds spread these pollutants around the northern hemisphere.

Sulphur dioxide dissolves in water in the air to form lots of tiny droplets of sulphuric acid. These droplets reflect radiation from the Sun and less energy reaches the surface of the Earth. The summer months of 1816 were up to 3 °C cooler than normal. This caused crop failures and famines, and over 200 000 people died in Europe alone.

D *Dust from volcanoes scatters light in the atmosphere and gives colourful sunsets. This photo was taken after the eruption of Mount Pinatubo in 1991.*

4 a What effect can a large volcanic eruption have on the average world temperature?
  b How does it cause this effect? (*Hint:* there are two ways.)
5 Why did people die around the world as a result of the Tambora eruption?
6 How would wildlife have been affected in 1816? Use ideas about energy and food chains in your answer. **H S W**

I CAN...

o explain why rainwater is naturally acidic.
o describe how a volcanic eruption can affect climate.
o describe the effect of volcanic pollution on food chains. **H S W**

What are the causes and effects of acid rain?

Rain is naturally slightly acidic because carbon dioxide dissolves in it. However, over the last 200 years our rainwater has become even more acidic, with the pH sometimes dropping as low as 3. This has mainly been caused by air pollution from burning **fossil fuels**.

All fossil fuels contain some sulphur, and burning them releases sulphur dioxide. The high temperatures produced inside car engines also make nitrogen and oxygen combine to produce nitrogen oxides. Sulphur dioxide and nitrogen oxides dissolve in water to form acids, so the rain becomes even more acidic than normal. Rain with a pH below 5.6 is called **acid rain**, and can cause serious environmental problems. Acid rain can kill trees. It also speeds up the **chemical weathering** of carbonate rocks such as limestone, and causes metals to **corrode**.

> **!** The amount of sulphur dioxide that falls as acid rain on Britain is far less than the amount that is released into the air. Most of the rest falls on other parts of Europe such as Sweden.

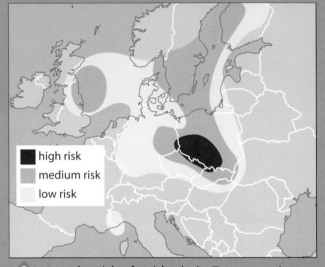

high risk
medium risk
low risk

A *How the risk of acid rain in Europe varies.*

B *Trees killed by acid rain.*

1 Rainwater is naturally acidic. Explain what 'acid rain' is.
2 What causes acid rain?
3 Name two different types of material that are affected by acid rain.

Acid rain running into lakes lowers the pH of the lake water, which can kill water organisms. The acidity can be **neutralised** by adding powdered lime to the lakes.

Some organisms are not directly affected by acidic water in rivers or lakes. However, they can die if organisms nearer the start of their food chain are killed.

> **!** Sweden spends around €200 000 each year on adding powdered lime to its lakes. The lime, however, can cause other problems, like killing sphagnum moss growing near lakes.

Acid rain reacts with substances in the soil. Some of these reactions cause mineral salts (which plants need to grow) to wash out of the soil. Other reactions produce poisonous compounds that kill plants and can wash into rivers and lakes.

In recent years many governments around the world have passed laws to control air pollution from all sources, including cars and power stations. For example, fossil fuel power stations now have **sulphur precipitators** fitted to their chimneys, which remove sulphur dioxide from the waste gases. Diesel and petrol are now produced with less sulphur in them, and **catalytic converters** in vehicle exhaust systems convert exhaust gases to less harmful ones. As a result, emissions of gases in the UK that cause acid rain have halved since 1990.

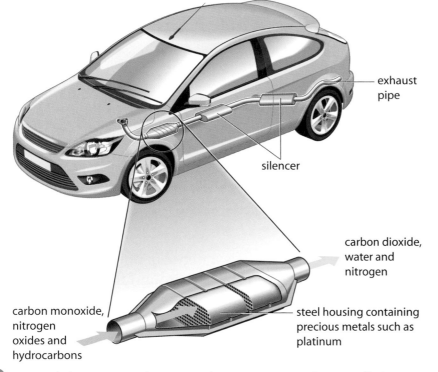

D A catalytic converter in a car exhaust system reduces pollution.

exhaust pipe

silencer

carbon dioxide, water and nitrogen

carbon monoxide, nitrogen oxides and hydrocarbons

steel housing containing precious metals such as platinum

4 What does acid rain do to soil?
5 How does acid rain affect life in rivers and lakes? Explain as fully as you can.

C The MOT test for cars includes measuring car exhaust gases. If the levels of polluting gases are too high, the car fails the test and cannot be driven on the roads.

!

A 'publicity stunt' is when a company does something out of the ordinary to get news coverage. In 2005 a British bus company 'joked' that their buses were being fitted with tanks of sheep urine to act as catalytic converters. This made news around the world. In fact they were experimenting with a converter using urea. This substance is found in urine but they were using an artificial source.

6 Describe two different ways in which the UK's emissions of harmful gases can be reduced. Ⓗ Ⓢ Ⓦ
7 Catalytic converters reduce pollution but they are expensive. Suggest why they are fitted to cars in spite of the expense. Ⓗ Ⓢ Ⓦ
8 Look at map A. Ⓗ Ⓢ Ⓦ
  a Suggest why there is more acid rain in Sweden than in the UK.
  b Why should the UK try to reduce emissions of harmful gases?

I CAN...

o explain what causes acid rain.
o describe the effects of acid rain.
o explain how acid rain can be reduced, and why we should do this. Ⓗ Ⓢ Ⓦ

Is the amount of pollution changing?

Air pollution is a serious problem for all living things, including humans. Scientists need to **monitor** pollution to find out where it is coming from. They need to work out the best ways of preventing pollution in the future and of cleaning up polluted areas. So that they can evaluate whether methods of trying to control pollution are working, they need to know what pollution was like in the past.

The scientific monitoring of air only began about 100 years ago. To find out about pollution before this we need to use other methods. Air pollution affects the weather and it affects people's health. Breathing in tiny airborne particles can lead to heart disease or breathing problems, for example. Looking at weather records and health records can give information about pollution levels.

B An automatic air quality monitoring station in London.

HowScienceWorks

A Taking a water sample to measure pollution.

1 Why do scientists need to monitor pollution?
2 Describe one way of finding out about pollution in the past.

Today, there is a network of air quality monitoring stations around the UK. Different monitoring stations provide us with information on different pollutants. For example, some monitoring stations collect and test rainwater for pH and certain chemicals. Other monitoring stations filter the air to trap tiny particles of soot or other solid materials. The amount of material on the filter is measured by seeing how much light is reflected by the used filter.

3 How could you monitor acid rain in your local area?

The data from all the monitoring stations is collected and analysed, and it is made available in libraries and on the internet. Local and national governments use the information to decide how to control pollution. The data is also used to produce forecasts of **air quality**. People who are sensitive to pollution (e.g. because they have asthma) can use air quality forecasts to help them to decide whether or not to go out on certain days.

4 a What problems can be caused by particles in the air?
  b Why can small particles be more dangerous than bigger ones?
5 a Look at graph C. How has the amount of pollution caused by tiny particles changed in the UK since 1970?
  b Suggest some reasons for these changes.
6 Why are air quality forecasts needed?

There are other ways to estimate air quality. For example, levels of sulphur dioxide affect certain lichens. If there are no lichens then this usually means the air is polluted. This way of monitoring air pollution does not need a lab and it gives a good picture of the overall health of the environment. Similarly, the numbers and types of animals living in streams can be used to indicate the quality of the water in the stream.

7 Suggest some advantages of using an animal or plant survey instead of a chemical analysis to assess levels of pollution.

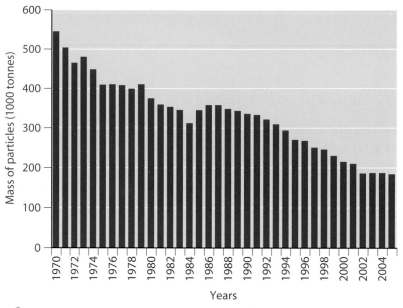

C Emissions of particles less than 0.01 mm diameter in the UK. These small particles are more harmful than bigger ones, as they can get further into the lungs.

How could you investigate the amount of particles in the air in your town? Which places would you investigate?

D These lichens can only grow in clean air with very low levels of sulphur dioxide.

I CAN...

o explain why air pollution needs to be monitored.
o describe different ways in which air pollution can be monitored.

Is the Earth getting warmer?

HowScienceWorks

Greenhouse gases in the Earth's atmosphere can trap heat in the atmosphere and so warm up the atmosphere. Without this warming effect, called the **greenhouse effect**, the Earth would be much colder than it is today. Greenhouse gases include carbon dioxide, water vapour and methane (which is produced in the digestive systems of animals like cows).

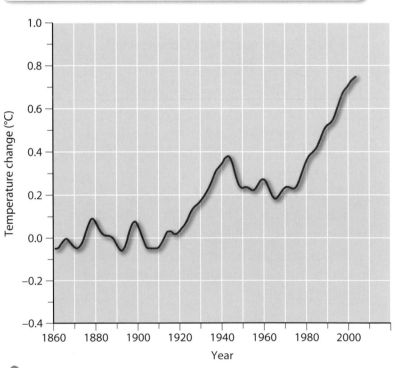

Some heat is reflected and lost.

solar radiation

The warm Earth radiates heat.

Some heat is absorbed by the carbon dioxide in the atmosphere and re-radiated back to the surface.

reaches surface

Most heat is absorbed by surface of Earth.

Earth

A *The greenhouse effect.*

There is scientific evidence that our climate is changing. Graph B shows how the mean world temperature has changed since 1860.

The graph shows only a small increase in air temperature, about 0.6 °C, between 1900 and 2000. However, as the rise has been greatest in the last 20 years, many scientists think there will be a much greater rise during this century. Some predict a rise of up to 5 °C in the next 100 years.

If this level of **global warming** happens, the ice in Antarctica will melt and make sea levels rise significantly. This would flood many coastal areas. Weather patterns would change, and although the mean temperature of the Earth would rise, it could actually become colder in some places. For this reason, the effect is sometimes referred to as **climate change**.

1 Give two reasons why we need carbon dioxide in the atmosphere.

2 Name two other greenhouse gases.

B *Change in mean world temperature from 1860 to 2004. The temperatures are compared to the mean temperature in 1900.*

3 Why is 'climate change' a more accurate term than 'global warming'?

Most scientists believe that rising temperatures are linked to increasing carbon dioxide levels in the atmosphere. Carbon dioxide levels are going up because we are burning more fossil fuels, and destroying forests that use up the gas during photosynthesis. However, not all scientists agree. Some think that world temperatures will change anyway, and that they may even fall in the future.

Scientists use **computer models** to help them to predict how the climate might change. The scientists input how much carbon dioxide is likely to be added to the atmosphere in the future. The models are then used to work out how this carbon dioxide will affect the climate.

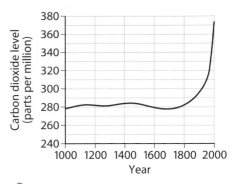

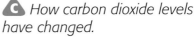

C *How carbon dioxide levels have changed.*

The Swedish scientist Svante Arrhenius (1859–1927) published a paper in 1896 in which he suggested that carbon dioxide being added to the atmosphere by burning fossil fuels could cause the Earth to warm up.

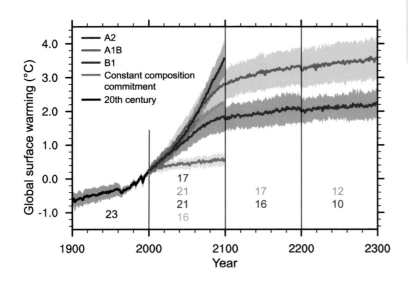

D *These predictions were published in 2007. The different coloured lines from 2000 onwards are based on different assumptions about the amounts of carbon dioxide that will be put into the air. The coloured numbers show how many different computer models have been used to make the predictions.*

E *An artist's interpretation of global warming.*

4 a What do most scientists believe is causing global warming?
  b Suggest why they think this.
5 How do scientists predict how the climate may change in the future?
6 Look at drawing E.
  a How does this represent global warming?
  b The image is to be used on a poster trying to persuade people to cut the amount of carbon dioxide they produce. How effective do you think it would be? Explain your answer.

I CAN...

o describe the effects of carbon dioxide in the atmosphere.
o explain what climate change means.
o describe how climate predictions are made.

How has the temperature of the Earth changed over time?

HowScienceWorks

Most scientists agree that global warming is happening because humans are putting more carbon dioxide into the atmosphere. One of the reasons for this agreement is that changes in global temperature in the past appear to be linked to changes in carbon dioxide concentration.

One way of finding out about the atmosphere in the past is to examine how much carbon dioxide there is in bubbles of air trapped in ice in Antarctica. Each winter a new layer of ice is laid down, so scientists can work out how old each bubble of air is by counting the layers. Scientists drill an **ice core** and carefully extract the gases.

A Scientists extracting an ice core.

Temperatures on Earth can also be estimated from ice cores. Some atoms of oxygen are heavier than others, which means that water molecules (which include an oxygen atom) can also have slightly different masses. When the climate is warm, more of the heavier water molecules can evaporate. Some of these molecules eventually fall again as snow. This snow becomes ice when it is buried by further falls of snow. Scientists can estimate temperatures in the past by carefully measuring the proportion of light and heavy water molecules in the ice.

1 Are the oldest layers of ice at the top or bottom of an ice core? Explain your answer.

2 Suggest some precautions that scientists should take to make sure their results for the composition of the atmosphere in the past are reliable.

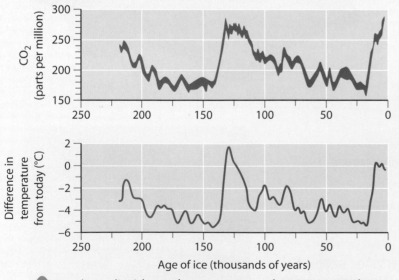

B Carbon dioxide and temperature changes over the last 200 000 years, from ice core analysis. Carbon dioxide concentration has today risen to a level of 360 ppm.

The ice core containing the oldest ice was drilled by the European Project for Ice Coring in Antarctica (EPICA) at Concordia Station in Antarctica. The core can provide data for the last 740 000 years. Funding for EPICA is provided by ten European countries.

3 Look at the graphs in B.
  a Over the last 200 000 years, has the Earth mainly been warmer or colder than it is today?
  b How do the levels of carbon dioxide in the past compare with today's level?

Scientists check the reliability of their temperature estimates by using other ways of estimating the temperature. One way of doing this is by looking at pollen grains preserved in the mud at the bottom of lakes. By examining the numbers of different kinds of pollen grain found in the mud, scientists can work out the kind of plants that lived near the lake at different times in the past. They can look at the same types of plants living today and the temperatures that they grow in. This gives a good idea of what the temperatures were in the past.

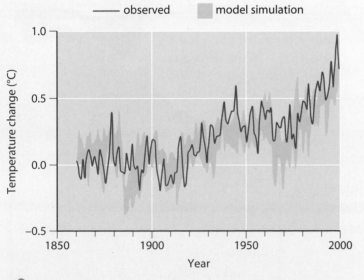

C *Different types of pollen grain.*

Scientists need to evaluate how accurate their computer climate models are. One way of doing this is to start the model using conditions at some time in the past, and allow it to 'predict' changes that have already happened.

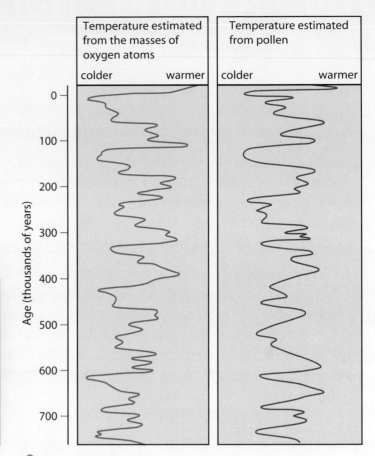

D *The pollen information can't tell us the actual temperatures, but it does show that both ways of estimating the temperature show warm and cold periods at approximately the same times.*

E *The results of a model run by the Hadley Centre for Climate Prediction and Research.*

4 Why do scientists use more than one method to estimate temperatures in the past?

5 Suggest why examining pollen cannot give exact temperatures for periods in the past.

6 Look at graph E.
  a Suggest why the line for the model simulation is quite wide.
  b How reliable do you think the simulation is?

HowScienceWorks

How can we try to reduce pollution and climate change?

Pollution and global warming are problems for everyone on the Earth. Pollution produced in one country can affect other countries. Global warming is likely to affect everyone in some way. Some people will be affected more than others.

The International Panel on Climate Change (IPCC) includes climate scientists and representatives from governments around the world. It looks at all the research carried out on climate change around the world. The IPCC produces reports at regular intervals, and governments use these reports to help them to decide what should be done to help to reduce the causes and effects of climate change.

We all need to try to do something to reduce pollution and global warming – but who should be doing most?

A Cutting carbon emissions would damage our economy. Why should we cut our emissions while countries like India and China are increasing theirs?

B Our economy is still developing. We cannot afford to spend money on cutting pollution or developing renewable energy resources. We deserve the same lifestyle as people in the West.

C Each person in the US is responsible for about eight times as much carbon dioxide as each Chinese person. And nearly a third of our manufacturing is bought by the West!

D We are not a rich country – we need to earn money from our rainforests. If you want us to stop clearing them, you must help us to get the money we need in other ways.

1 a Write down some natural sources of pollution.
  b Write down some sources of pollution caused by humans.
  c What effects can these different kinds of pollution have?
2 Suggest some ways in which pollution can be reduced.
3 Explain why pollution needs to be monitored.
4 a What causes global warming?
  b How could global warming affect us?

HAVE YOUR SAY

Who should take the responsibility for cutting greenhouse gas emissions?
Should developing nations be asked to cut their emissions?

HowScienceWorks

Louis Blériot (1872–1936) became the first man to fly across the English Channel in 1909. His aeroplane was made from wood and steel wires, with linen cloth covering the wings. Modern aircraft are built using many different materials, carefully selected for their **properties**.

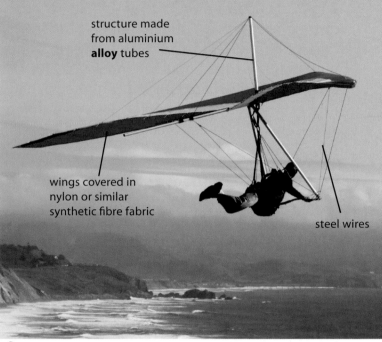

structure made from aluminium **alloy** tubes

wings covered in nylon or similar synthetic fibre fabric

steel wires

B A hang glider.

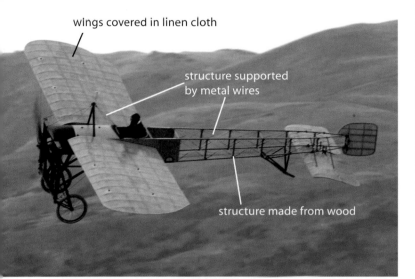

wings covered in linen cloth

structure supported by metal wires

structure made from wood

A A modern replica of Blériot's Type XI aeroplane. It has a top speed of 47 mph.

C An Airbus A380 can carry over 850 passengers. It is made of aluminium alloys and **composite** materials such as carbon-fibre reinforced plastic and glass-fibre reinforced plastic.

1 a List as many differences as you can between Blériot's aeroplane and a modern airliner.
  b Why are the two aeroplanes made of different materials? Give as many reasons as you can.

2 a List the properties of wood.
  b List the properties of metal.
  c Suggest why most modern aeroplanes have frames made from metal.

3 Suggest why the hang glider has wings made from:
  a nylon rather than cotton.
  b nylon rather than sheets of metal.

How can the properties of materials be improved?

Engineers and designers choose materials because of their properties. For example, rubber is used for tyres because it is flexible. Rubber is a **natural** material. It is made of very long molecules called **polymers**, which are tangled together. When the rubber is stretched the molecules straighten out. When the stretching force is removed the molecules spring back to their normal shape.

In its natural state rubber becomes very soft and sticky in the summer, and hard and brittle in the winter. We could not use rubber with these properties for things like car tyres. The properties of rubber can be changed by a process called **vulcanisation**. The rubber is heated with sulphur, and a reaction occurs that forms cross-links between the long molecules. These cross-links make the rubber much harder and tougher, and stop its properties changing with changing temperature.

A Tyres often get hot enough to smoke when an aeroplane lands.

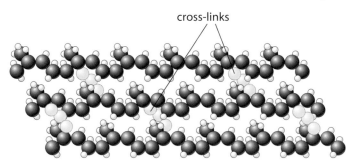

B Rubber is obtained from rubber tree sap.

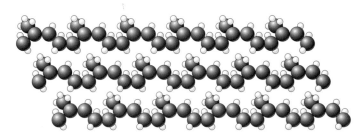

C In natural rubber, some molecules can slide over each other, so the rubber does not always go back to its original shape after stretching. A material that keeps a new shape is said to be **plastic**.

cross-links

In vulcanised rubber, the cross-links stop the molecules sliding past each other, so the rubber is more **elastic** (it goes back to its original shape when the stretching force is removed).

1 Why is natural rubber unsuitable for vehicle tyres? Explain in as much detail as you can.

2 How does vulcanising help to improve the properties of rubber?

3 What do you think would happen to the rubber if too many cross-links were formed between the molecules?

4 a Which do you think has the most cross-links: the rubber used in car tyres or the rubber used in elastic bands? Explain your answer. **H S W**

b How could you find out if you are correct? **H S W**

Rubber is just one example of a natural polymer. Protein and starch molecules are polymers, and so are fibres such as wool, silk and **cellulose** (found in cotton and other plant cell walls). Many objects that used to be made with natural materials can now be made with **synthetic** polymers. These are made in reactions that join lots of small molecules (called **monomers**) together into long chains. Synthetic polymers are often cheaper to produce and have more useful properties than natural polymers.

H S W

Hermann Staudinger (1881–1965) was the first chemist to suggest that very long chains of molecules could exist, held together by strong chemical bonds. He presented his theory at a meeting of the Zurich Chemical Society in 1926. He was awarded the Nobel Prize for chemistry in 1953.

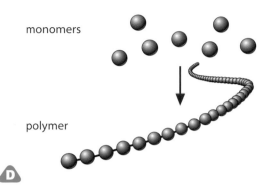

monomers

polymer

D

E *The first hot air balloon flight with passengers was in 1783. The balloon was made from silk lined with paper.*

One of the most commonly used synthetic polymers is nylon, first produced in 1935 by Wallace Carothers (1896–1937).

F *The first parachutes were made from silk. During World War II parachutes were made from nylon instead, as there was not enough silk available.*

5 a Suggest why the first hot air balloons were made from silk and paper.
  b What do you think modern hot air balloons are made from?
6 a What are the properties of silk and nylon that make them suitable materials for parachutes?
  b Why do you think silk was in short supply during World War II?
7 Describe how you could find out if nylon or silk is best for making a parachute.   H S W

I CAN...

o describe how the properties of rubber can be modified.
o explain why synthetic materials are often used instead of natural materials.   H S W

How can materials be combined to improve their properties?

Synthetic polymers can be moulded to make objects of many different shapes. They are often referred to as 'plastics' in everyday life. The **raw materials** for most synthetic polymers come from oil.

1 What is a polymer?
2 Look at photo A. Ⓗ Ⓢ Ⓦ
   a What do you think some of the properties of Bakelite are?
   b Explain your answer.
3 Make a list of five different things in your home that are made from polymers (or plastics).
4 For each item you wrote down in question **3**:
   a describe the important properties of the polymer for that use.
   b suggest a different material that could have been used for the same object.
   c write down the advantages and disadvantages of the two materials. Ⓗ Ⓢ Ⓦ

A *Bakelite was the first widely used synthetic polymer. It was invented by Leo Baekeland (1863– 1944), and started selling in 1909. It was used to make many different things, including electrical switches, cups and even propellers!*

Many polymers can be made into fibres (long threads) by forcing the liquid polymer through tiny holes. There are many different kinds of polymer fibre in use today.

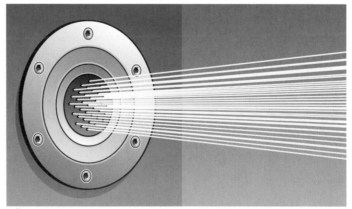

B *Synthetic polymer fibres being made.*

Kevlar is a polymer fibre that is five times stronger than the same weight of steel. Kevlar's most well known use is in bullet-proof vests. The Kevlar fibre is woven into cloth, and the vest is made using several layers of this cloth. The fibres are so strong that they do not break if a bullet hits the vest. They also help to spread out the force from the bullet to reduce bruising injuries.

C *Kevlar can be used in motorcycle tyres, brakes and other components, and in boots, jackets, gloves and helmets. Some people are willing to pay the higher price for the advantages of using Kevlar.*

5 How are polymers made into fibres?
6 a Write down two properties of Kevlar.
   b Explain why these two properties are important for making bullet-proof vests.

Composite materials are made from two different materials with very different properties. One material is a strong but flexible mat, woven from fibres of a material like Kevlar. The other material is a liquid that is painted onto layers of the matting. When it is heated, this liquid sets into a rigid but brittle material called the 'matrix'. Fibres made from glass or carbon can also be used in composite materials.

Lightweight but strong items such as sports equipment and parts of aircraft can be made using composite materials. Objects made from these materials are safe to use, but workers making the objects need to wear facemasks, gloves and overalls to stop them breathing in bits of fibre or coming into contact with the matrix material.

F Voyager *made the first non-stop round the world flight in December 1986. Its flight lasted just over nine days. Most of* Voyager *was made from composite materials.*

In 2008 the protective clothing company Miguel Caballero launched a range of bullet-proof clothing in the UK. Prices start from £3000!

D

E *Making a composite yacht. Mats made from woven fibres are put onto a mould, and liquid resin is applied. This will set to form a rigid shape when it is heated.*

7 Explain which part of a composite material you think is important for:
   a resisting tension (pulling) forces.
   b resisting compression (squashing) forces.
   c keeping the object the correct shape.
8 Suggest why composite materials were used to build *Voyager*.

I CAN...

o recall some properties and uses of different polymers.

o compare the properties of polymers with other materials.

o explain what a composite material is.

How can aircraft be made safer?

HowScienceWorks

Aircraft may crash for many reasons. Sometimes crashes occur because of something wrong with the material the aircraft is made from. Every time an aircraft crashes, there is an investigation to find out the cause of the crash. The results of these investigations often lead to new ways of using materials, to the modification of materials, or to the development of new materials.

The *Hindenburg* was a German airship that took passengers across the Atlantic Ocean between Europe and the USA. It caught fire as it was coming in to land in New Jersey in 1937, and burned completely within a minute.

It is still not certain what caused the fire, or why the airship burned so rapidly. The *Hindenburg* was filled with hydrogen to make it float, and some people say this was responsible for the fire. Other people point to the material covering the airship. This was cotton cloth painted with a flammable paint that included aluminium powder. Aluminium powder is also flammable, but was included to make the airship reflective.

A *Air accident investigators piece together bits of crashed aeroplanes to help them to work out why the crash happened.*

1 Modern airships are filled with helium, not hydrogen. Suggest why helium is used today.

2 Suggest why the *Hindenburg* was painted with reflective paint.

3 One organisation supporting the 'flammable fabric' idea is the National Hydrogen Association. Suggest why their opinion might be biased.

B *The* Hindenburg *on fire.*

The de Havilland Comet was the world's first commercial airliner powered by jet engines. In January 1954, a Comet broke up in flight over the sea, killing everyone on board. The committee investigating the cause of the crash made their report before most of the wreckage had been recovered. They concluded that a fire was probably the cause of the crash. Comets started flying again in March, after some modifications to improve protection against fire. Then, on 8th April, another Comet crashed over the sea.

This time more intensive investigations were carried out, and it was discovered that the square windows caused forces in the skin to concentrate near the window corners, and this had made a crack. The material was not changed, but the Comet was redesigned to have oval windows.

> 4 The two Comet crashes happened over the sea. How did this make the investigation into the cause more difficult?
>
> 5 Do you think that Comets should have been allowed to fly again in March 1954? Explain your answer.
>
> 6 a Why do modern airliners have small, oval windows for the passengers?
>   b Explain why the windows at the front of airliners are much bigger.

D *A crash in Sao Paulo, Brazil, in July 2007.*

Many aircraft crashes happen because something goes wrong with the landing. If the aircraft hits an obstacle which damages the fuel tanks, the fuel on board may catch fire. Photo E shows a test of a new chemical added to the aeroplane's fuel. The chemical was supposed to stop the kerosene fuel forming an explosive mist if the aeroplane crashed.

E *This aeroplane was landed by remote control. Stakes were put in the ground to deliberately damage the wings and fuel tanks.*

> 7 Liquid kerosene burns, but it does not explode.
>   a What could happen in a crash to make kerosene explode?
>   b Do you think the additive is in use today?
>
> 8 Some aircraft are fitted with 'fuel tank inerting' systems, which fill the space above the fuel in a tank with nitrogen. Suggest how this helps to prevent fires.

What happens to chemicals in a reaction?

Many manufacturing companies employ scientists to invent new materials with better properties than existing materials. To make a new material with a particular set of properties, chemists need to work out which chemicals to react together. Once they have worked out the reaction to use to make a new material, they also need to work out *how much* of each **reactant** is needed to make the **product** they want.

Photo B shows what happens if you mix lead nitrate solution with potassium iodide solution. If you measured the mass of the products of the reaction, you would find it was exactly the same as the mass of the reactants you started with.

A *A scientist testing the properties of a new plastic material.*

B potassium iodide   +   lead nitrate   →   solid lead iodide in potassium nitrate solution

1 Look at photo B.
   a What are the reactants in this reaction?
   b What are the products?
2 If the total mass of the reactants was 30 g, what would the mass of the products be? **H S W**

HSW

How could you find out if the mass of the reactants is the same as the mass of the products of a reaction?
● What apparatus would you need?

C iron filings

Mass is never gained or lost in a chemical reaction. This idea is known as the **law of conservation of mass**. When a reaction happens, the atoms in the chemicals are rearranged into different compounds. No new atoms are created and no atoms can disappear. The same law applies to physical changes such as changes of state or dissolving.

3 If you reacted 2 g of hydrogen with 16 g of oxygen, what mass of water would you get? **H S W**
4 a If you melted 25 g of ice, what mass of water would you get? **H S W**
   b Is this a physical change or a chemical reaction?

Hydrogen and oxygen react to form water. This reaction is used to power some spacecraft. There are exactly the same numbers of hydrogen and oxygen atoms present before and after the reaction, they are just combined in a different way.

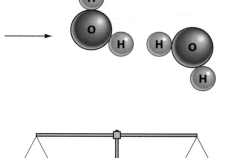

D

Sometimes it seems as if mass is gained in a reaction. For instance, if you heat zinc in air you get a white powder. The mass of the white powder is greater than the mass of the zinc you started with. The zinc has combined with oxygen from the air to form zinc oxide. The mass of the zinc and the oxygen that reacted would be the same as the mass of the zinc oxide.

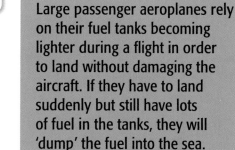

zinc + oxygen   zinc oxide

E   ● oxygen ○ zinc

5 a Write a word equation for the reaction of zinc with oxygen.
   b If you made 8.1 g of zinc oxide from 6.5 g of zinc, what mass of oxygen has reacted? Ⓗ Ⓢ Ⓦ

In other reactions, it can sometimes seem as if mass is lost. The gas cylinder that supplies the burner for the hot air balloon in photo F gradually gets lighter. The mass of the gas it contains seems to have disappeared. The gas combines with oxygen in the air to form carbon dioxide gas, which escapes into the air.

! Large passenger aeroplanes rely on their fuel tanks becoming lighter during a flight in order to land without damaging the aircraft. If they have to land suddenly but still have lots of fuel in the tanks, they will 'dump' the fuel into the sea.

F

6 Look at this word equation:
   magnesium + hydrochloric acid →
     magnesium chloride + hydrogen
   a How would the mass of the chemicals seem to change in this reaction? Ⓗ Ⓢ Ⓦ
   b Explain your answer to part a.
7 When plants grow their mass increases. Where does the extra mass come from?

I CAN...

o explain why mass is conserved in a reaction.
o explain why some reactions seem to lose or gain mass.

How can we use chemical reactions as energy resources?

Many scientists used to think that materials contained a substance called **phlogiston** ('*flo-jist-on*'). When materials burned the phlogiston escaped, leaving a solid ash called a **calx**. This theory explained why the mass of the ash from burning coal was less than the original mass of the coal.

We now know that **fuels** combine with oxygen during **combustion**. However, even after oxygen was discovered in 1772, some scientists still thought that phlogiston was released – this explained the heat and light given off. Today we know that these are forms of energy that are transferred.

Many fuels, like kerosene, are **hydrocarbons**. The word equation shows what happens when kerosene burns.

kerosene + oxygen ➔ carbon dioxide + water

H S W

How could you find out what chemicals are formed when you burn other fuels containing hydrogen and carbon?
- Which fuels will you use?
- How will you test the products of the reaction?

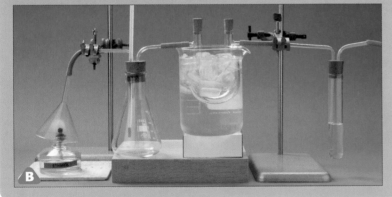
B

Other chemicals are also used as fuels. Hydrogen gas burns to produce water, and can be used in cars and rockets. Many people think that hydrogen is a better fuel than hydrocarbons, because it does not produce carbon dioxide, which contributes to global warming. However, it is highly explosive if it is mixed with air, and it needs to be compressed (squashed) to store it.

A The energy needed to power this aircraft is stored in kerosene fuel. Every kilogram of kerosene releases about 44 000 kJ of energy when it burns.

1 Why is petrol called a hydrocarbon?
2 Which element from the air combines with a hydrocarbon when it burns?
3 Which compounds are formed when a hydrocarbon burns?
4 What chemicals will be in the exhaust from the engines of the fighter aircraft in photo A?
5 a Write down one advantage of using hydrogen as a fuel in a car. H S W
  b Write down two disadvantages. H S W

The solid rocket boosters in photo C do not use hydrogen or oxygen. Instead the fuel is aluminium metal and the oxygen is provided by a chemical called ammonium perchlorate. During the reaction the ammonium perchlorate releases oxygen atoms that combine with aluminium atoms. The reaction releases energy.

> **6** Look at photos A and C. Suggest why hydrogen is used in rockets rather than kerosene.

Virgin Galactic's *SpaceShipTwo* is to take tourists into space. Its fuel is rubbery polymer, which reacts with oxygen atoms from a gas called nitrous oxide.

C The Ariane rocket uses liquid hydrogen in its main engines. Every kilogram of hydrogen releases about 140 000 kJ of energy when it burns. The rocket also carries liquid oxygen to allow the combustion reaction to happen.

D An artist's impression of what SpaceShipTwo *might look like in flight.*

Chemicals can be used as energy resources even if they do not burn. The chemicals inside batteries produce electricity when they are put into a circuit.

E This aeroplane is powered by 160 AA batteries! It flew for nearly a minute in 2006, and covered nearly 400 metres.

> **7** Cars can also be powered using batteries. Suggest why a battery powered car is more practical than a battery powered aeroplane.

I CAN...

- describe two different theories for burning.   H S W
- recall the compounds made when hydrocarbon fuels burn.
- describe the advantages and disadvantages of different fuels.   H S W

How Science Works

Are aeroplanes necessary?

Millions of people fly in aeroplanes every year, on holiday or on business, and the numbers are increasing. Some people think that all this air travel is unnecessary and harmful.

A *Airliners queuing up for take-off.*

B *A fighter aircraft dropping bombs.*

> Airlines put polluting gases high into the atmosphere, where they make an even bigger contribution to global warming.

> Airlines don't have to pay tax on the fuel they use – that's not fair!

> Cheap flights are great – we go sunbathing in Spain twice a year.

> How would we get help to disaster zones quickly without aeroplanes?

> Some of the newest airliners can carry over 800 passengers. Think of the loss of life if one of those crashed!

> Seeing other cultures helps us to understand their problems.

> Aeroplanes are used to fly into hurricanes to investigate how they work.

> Aeroplanes are used to drop bombs – we would be better off without them!

> What would happen if we banned planes and everyone drove across Europe for their holidays?

> Aeroplanes allow countries in the developing world to earn money by exporting fresh vegetables.

HAVE YOUR SAY

Would the world be better off if there were fewer aeroplanes?

What information would you need to help you to make a decision?

1 Many companies that manufacture aeroplanes research new materials. Explain the kinds of properties that these new materials should have.

2 Why do chemists developing new materials need to know what happens in reactions?

Buying energy

Ⓗow Ⓢcience Ⓦorks

We all need energy in our homes for heating, lighting and cooking. The energy has to be paid for. Most people would prefer to have smaller electricity and gas bills!

The electricity supplied to homes and schools is **mains electricity**, which is **generated** in power stations. Most power stations burn **fossil fuels** to make the electricity. Burning these fuels adds carbon dioxide to the atmosphere. Most scientists agree that adding carbon dioxide to the atmosphere is causing **global warming**.

B *Dale Vince set up a company that generates electricity using energy stored in the wind.*

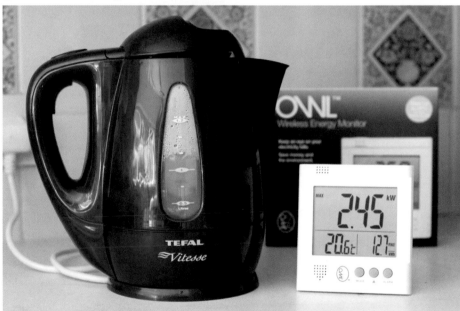

A *This monitor allows you to see how much electricity you are using and how much it costs.*

Drax power station is the largest coal-fired power station in the UK. On average it uses 20 train-loads of coal per day. Each train delivers around 1400 tonnes of coal.

C

1 **a** What is global warming?
   b Why will global warming cause problems?
2 Fossil fuels are **energy resources**.
   a Write down some of the uses of fossil fuels.
   b Explain why we should reduce the amount of fossil fuels we use.
   c What other energy resources can be used to generate electricity?
3 Suggest some ways in which you can reduce the amount of fossil fuels you use.
4 The energy monitor shown in photo A has to be plugged in to work. Suggest how it can help to *reduce* the amount of electricity you use.

How is energy stored and moved?

Electricity is a way of **transferring** energy (moving it from one place to another). Energy can also be transferred through:

- heating
- forces
- sound
- light and **infrared radiation**.

Fossil fuels are **energy resources** because they can transfer energy when they combine with oxygen. We refer to the energy stored in fossil fuels as **chemical energy**. Food and cells (batteries) are also stores of chemical energy.

When fossil fuels burn, energy is transferred as heat. In photo A, chemical energy stored in the **natural gas** is transferred as heat to the water in the pan. The water now has a store of **thermal energy**. The pan itself and the air around it also heat up.

> **1** Write down three things that:
> **a** transfer energy by heating or light.
> **b** transfer energy by sound.
> **c** use energy transferred by electricity.

A

> **2** Natural gas stores chemical energy. Write down four other things that are stores of chemical energy.

Energy can be stored in other ways. **Nuclear** (or **atomic**) **energy** is stored inside atoms. Nuclear power stations can transfer the nuclear energy inside atoms of metals, such as uranium, to produce electricity. The Sun also contains a store of nuclear energy, some of which is transferred to the Earth as heat and light.

Moving objects are stores of energy, called **kinetic energy**. The faster the movement, the greater the kinetic energy.

Some kinds of stored energy are called **potential energy**. Stretched elastic bands store energy. This kind of potential energy is called **elastic potential energy**, or **strain energy**. Strain energy is stored whenever something is stretched, bent, twisted or squashed.

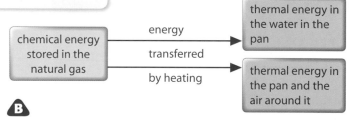

B

C This bow stores strain energy when it is bent. The energy is transferred to kinetic energy when the arrow is fired.

Anything in a high position stores **gravitational potential energy**. It took energy to move the object up to its high position, and this energy can be transferred again when the object falls.

> **3 a** Write down six different ways in which energy can be stored.
> **b** Give an example for each.

Look at diagram B again. The total amount of energy transferred when the natural gas combines with oxygen is the same as the total amount of thermal energy in the water, the pan and the surrounding air. Energy cannot be created or destroyed. This is called the **law of conservation of energy**.

The thermal energy in the water is **useful energy** – you wanted the *water* to be hot. The thermal energy in the pan and the air is **wasted energy**. The amount of useful energy stored at the end of the transfer compared to the total amount of energy transferred is the **efficiency**. An efficient machine does not waste much energy.

Our muscles are not very efficient. For every 100 J of chemical energy that a muscle transfers, only 25 J produce useful movement. The rest is transferred to heat, which ends up in the air around us. Our bodies are only 25% efficient.

D *The gravitational potential energy in this car is being transferred to kinetic energy as it falls.*

 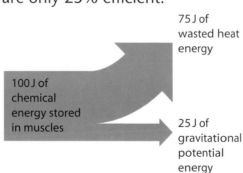

100 J of chemical energy stored in muscles

75 J of wasted heat energy

25 J of gravitational potential energy

E *This is a **Sankey diagram**. The width of each arrow shows the amount of energy it represents.*

> **4** Diagram B does not show all the ways in which energy is wasted. Redraw the diagram to show the other forms of wasted energy. **H S W**
> **5** The walker in photo E has 350 000 J of potential energy when she reaches the top of the hill. How much chemical energy have her muscles converted to:
> **a** useful energy? **b** wasted energy?
> **6** The Sankey diagram in E is a way of representing energy transfers. What are the advantages and disadvantages of this representation? **H S W**

A standard light bulb (with a filament) is about 9% efficient. An 'energy-saving' light bulb is about 45% efficient. Fireflies produce light using chemical energy from their food. They transfer the energy to light with an efficiency of 93%!

I CAN...

- describe ways in which energy is transferred and stored.
- draw a Sankey diagram. **H S** w
- explain what efficiency means.

How is electricity produced?

Electricity is **generated** in power stations. Power stations need an energy resource, such as fossil fuels, nuclear fuels, or a **renewable resource**.

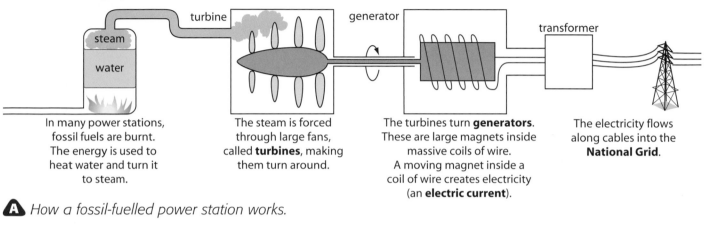

turbine   generator   transformer

steam
water

In many power stations, fossil fuels are burnt. The energy is used to heat water and turn it to steam.

The steam is forced through large fans, called **turbines**, making them turn around.

The turbines turn **generators**. These are large magnets inside massive coils of wire. A moving magnet inside a coil of wire creates electricity (an **electric current**).

The electricity flows along cables into the **National Grid**.

A How a fossil-fuelled power station works.

---

1 Where is electricity generated?   **2** How does a generator work?

A coal-fired power station is about 35% efficient. For every 100 J of chemical energy stored in the fuel, only about 35 J of electricity is produced. Some power stations that use natural gas can have an efficiency of over 50%.

3 An ordinary gas fire is only about 45% efficient, because some of the heat escapes through the flue (chimney). Draw a Sankey diagram to represent the energy transfers in a gas fire. **H S W**

4 Electric fires are nearly 100% efficient. A friend says that this means we should not use gas fires. Explain why he is wrong. **H S W**

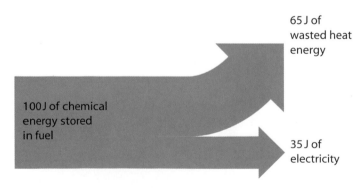

65 J of wasted heat energy

100 J of chemical energy stored in fuel

35 J of electricity

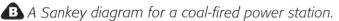

B A Sankey diagram for a coal-fired power station.

Nearly three quarters of the electricity generated in the UK is from fossil-fuelled power stations. Burning fossil fuels produces carbon dioxide, which contributes to **global warming**, and sulphur dioxide produced by burning coal can cause acid rain. Nuclear power stations do not produce carbon dioxide, but they cost a lot to build and produce dangerous radioactive substances that are difficult to store safely. **Biofuels** can also be used in power stations.

Stores of kinetic energy can also be used to generate electricity. For example the kinetic energy in the wind can be used to turn wind turbines. Moving water caused by waves or tides can also be used. **Hydroelectricity** is generated when water stored in a **reservoir** in the hills is allowed to flow down to a power station, where it makes the turbines spin.

Electricity flows from the power stations through a series of cables, called the National Grid. The National Grid contains over 20 000 km of overhead cables and over 1000 km of underground cables. That is enough cable to stretch halfway around the world.

Electricity cannot be stored, so power stations have to keep running all the time. Some hydroelectric power stations are **pumped storage** power stations. When there is plenty of spare electricity available at night, water is pumped up to the top reservoir. If there is a sudden demand for more electricity during the day, the water is allowed to run down the hill again. The water turns the turbines in the power station.

This is the Cruachan pumped storage power station in Scotland. **D**

> **!** Generators in power stations are filled with hydrogen for cooling. The hydrogen also gives less drag than air, so there is less friction inside the spinning generator.

H S W

Electricity can also be produced by cells. Very simple cells can be made using two pieces of metal dipped into a fruit juice.

- How would you find out which fruit juice worked best?
- What could you use instead of fruit juice?
- What other variables could you investigate?

C

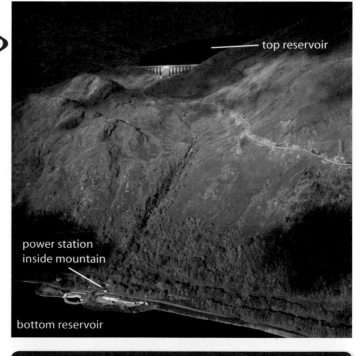
top reservoir

power station inside mountain

bottom reservoir

---

5 In what form is energy stored by the water in the top lake at the Cruachan power station?

6 Draw a table to show the advantages and disadvantages of using these energy resources to generate electricity: H S W
  a nuclear energy.   **b** fossil fuels.
  c wind.   **d** tides.

7 a Why is it important that fossil-fuelled power stations should be as efficient as possible? H S W
  b Why is efficiency less important for a wind turbine? H S W

I CAN...

- describe how electricity is generated.
- consider the advantages and disadvantages of different ways of generating electricity. H S w
- explain why efficiency is important. H S w

How much money can you save by using renewable resources?

Most people in the UK buy their gas and electricity from large companies. People can generate their own electricity by fitting solar cells to their roof, or by installing a wind turbine. However, these things cost money, so how do they decide if it is worth generating their own electricity?

One way of thinking about this is to look at the payback time. Generating your own electricity saves money because you will not need to buy as much electricity from the power companies. For example, if it cost £5000 to install a wind turbine, and it generated electricity worth £500 each year, it would take 10 years before you had paid back the price of the turbine. This 10 years is called the payback time. A wind turbine has an expected life of 20–30 years, so this turbine would save between £5000 and £10 000 overall, not allowing for any maintenance or repair costs.

HowScienceWorks

A

If a wind turbine generates more electricity than the owner uses, it can be sold to the National Grid. The actual savings will depend on how the price of electricity changes in the future.

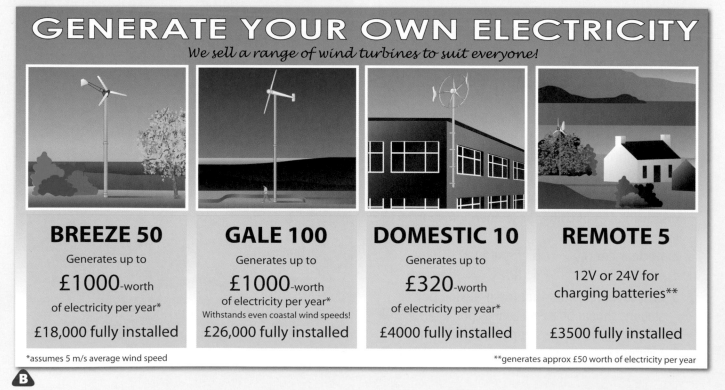

GENERATE YOUR OWN ELECTRICITY
We sell a range of wind turbines to suit everyone!

BREEZE 50

Generates up to

£1000-worth
of electricity per year*

£18,000 fully installed

GALE 100

Generates up to

£1000-worth
of electricity per year*
Withstands even coastal wind speeds!

£26,000 fully installed

DOMESTIC 10

Generates up to

£320-worth
of electricity per year*

£4000 fully installed

REMOTE 5

12V or 24V for
charging batteries**

£3500 fully installed

*assumes 5 m/s average wind speed

**generates approx £50 worth of electricity per year

B

1 Calculate the payback times for each of the wind turbines shown in advert B.

2 How will these payback times change if the price of electricity increases?

3 The value of the electricity generated by each turbine is not likely to be exactly as stated in the advert. Give as many reasons for this as you can.

4 Suggest why someone might buy the Gale 100 instead of the Breeze 50.

5 A hill farmer needs an electricity supply in a barn on a hillside. She calculates that the Remote 5 will have a payback time of 15 years. Suggest what additional factors she might be taking into account in this calculation.

!

The WhisperGen is a household boiler that can also generate electricity! It costs £3000, whereas a cheap boiler costs about £400. However, it contains a small engine that drives a generator so that, while it's heating your water and radiators, it's also generating electricity. If it generates more electricity than you use, the extra can be fed into the National Grid.

Energy payback times

Solar cells are another way in which householders can produce their own electricity, if they have a suitable area of roof.

For best performance, solar panels C *are put on south-facing roofs, at an angle of 35°. To get them performing at their best in winter a steeper angle (up to 75°) is better because the Sun is lower in the sky.*

Saves up to 1.2 tonnes of CO_2 per year, and over £350 on your electricity bills!

Only £9000 for the panels shown

The first solar cells manufactured were not very efficient, and did not last very long. In some cases, it took more energy to make the cells than they generated in their lifetime. Today's solar cells are much more efficient and last between 20 and 30 years. The time it takes to generate as much electricity as has been used to make the solar cells is called the **energy payback time**. The energy payback time for solar cells is between one and four years. Wind turbines do even better than this – the typical energy payback time for a wind turbine is several months.

6 a What does 'saves CO_2' mean?
  b Calculate the payback time for the solar cells shown in advert C.
  c Suggest why some people buy these panels.

7 Why do you think the energy payback time for wind turbines is so much less than for solar cells?

How are voltage and energy linked?

Electricity is a way of transferring energy (turning it from one form into another). An electric current is a flow of tiny particles called **electrons**. An electric circuit has:
- something to push the electrons around the circuit and to give them energy (such as a cell or **power pack**).
- a complete circuit for the current to flow around.
- **components** (like bulbs or buzzers) that transfer energy as light or sound.

The size of an electric current is measured using an **ammeter**. The units are **amps (A)**.

The **voltage** of a cell is a way of measuring how much energy the cell gives to the current. The voltage of a cell can be measured using a **voltmeter**. The units for voltage are **volts (V)**.

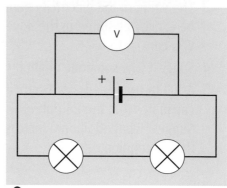

A The voltmeter is connected **in parallel** to the cell.

> **1** What are the units for voltage?

You can increase the voltage supplied to a circuit by:
- using more cells **in series**.
- using cells that supply a higher voltage.

If you increase the voltage supplied to the circuit and keep the rest of the components the same:
- the current increases.
- the amount of energy transferred by each amp of current increases.

> **2** Write down two ways to increase the voltage supplied to a circuit.
> **3** How does an increased voltage affect the circuit?

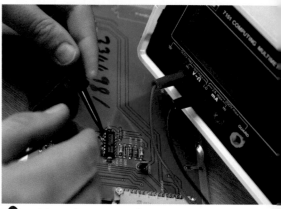

B This voltmeter is being used to check that the components are working properly.

Drawing C shows a model to help you to think about electricity.

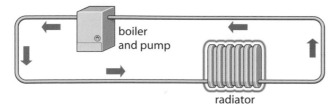

boiler and pump

radiator

C

> **4** Look at drawing C. Which part of the model represents: Ⓗ Ⓢ Ⓦ
>   **a** the cell **b** the wires
>   **c** a bulb?
>
> **5** You adjust the boiler so that it makes the water hotter, and pumps the water round the circuit faster. What change to the circuit do these changes to the model represent? Explain your answer. Ⓗ Ⓢ Ⓦ

Voltmeters can also be used to measure how much energy is converted by each component. The voltmeter is connected in parallel to a cell or component.

A **resistor** reduces the size of the current in a circuit by making it harder for current to flow. It transfers electrical energy to heat energy. In circuit D, the resistor is transferring the most energy to its surroundings. If you add up the voltages across the components the total should be the same as the voltage across the cell.

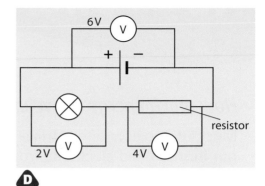

D

6 a The motor in circuit E is transferring 3 V of energy. What is the voltage across the resistor?

b Copy the circuit, and add a voltmeter that will measure the voltage supplied by the cell.

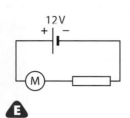

E

7 Photo G shows a restaurant with a belt that moves the food in front of you. You take the dishes that you want. Ⓗ Ⓢ Ⓦ

G

a Explain how this restaurant can be used as a model for a circuit.

b How could you adapt this model to help you to explain what happens when the voltage in a circuit is increased?

There are hundreds of resistors on the circuit boards of some appliances. Each one has coloured bands on it that tell you its resistance (how much harder it is for the current to flow).

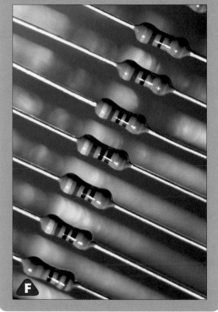

F

I CAN...

○ list the components in a circuit.

○ use a model to explain how changing the voltage affects a circuit. Ⓗ Ⓢ w

○ explain how to use a voltmeter.

How much energy do we use at home?

Most large pieces of electrical equipment in our homes need electricity from the mains supply. The mains supply provides electricity at 230 volts. This high voltage means that the electricity can transfer a lot of energy.

> **1** Look at photo A. Write down all the items that are using energy transferred by electricity.

The energy we use has to be paid for. The more energy we use, the higher the electricity bill! We can save money on electricity bills by switching things off when we do not need them, and by using more efficient appliances. Also, if we reduce the amount of electricity we use, we also reduce the amount of carbon dioxide put into the air by power stations.

Some appliances transfer more energy than others. An electric oven can transfer 5000 J of energy every second. Electric fires, hairdryers and kettles transfer 1000 J to 2000 J of electrical energy every second. Televisions and computers transfer up to about 400 J of energy every second. Light bulbs and radios transfer less than 100 J of energy each second.

> **2 a** Which household appliances transfer the most energy per second?
> **b** Which appliances transfer the least energy per second?
> **3** Which would save the most money: switching off the TV when you leave a room, or switching off a light? Explain your answer.
> **4** Which transfer the most energy: appliances that provide heat energy, or appliances that provide other forms of energy?

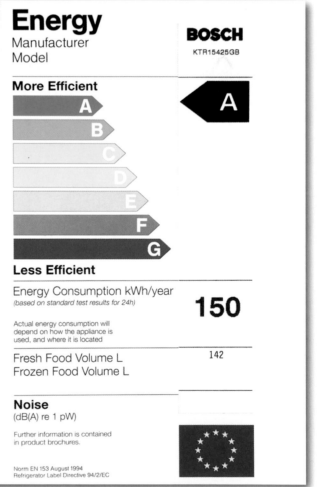

B *New appliances have energy labels to show how efficient they are. More efficient appliances are usually more expensive than less efficient ones.*

The **power** of an appliance is the number of joules of energy it transfers each second. The units for power are **watts**.

1 watt = 1 joule transferred every second.

Both of these light bulbs transfer 9 J of energy as light every second. The one on the left uses 20 J of energy to do this. The one on the right needs 100 J of energy to do this. The wasted energy is transferred by heating.

We can find out how much energy different appliances transfer by looking for their **power rating**. The higher the power rating, the more energy the appliance transfers each second.

5 a How will buying more efficient appliances help to cut electricity bills? Ⓗ Ⓢ Ⓦ

  b Explain how cutting electricity bills can also help the environment. Ⓗ Ⓢ Ⓦ

6 a Which bulb in photo C is the most efficient? Explain your answer. Ⓗ Ⓢ Ⓦ

  b Draw a Sankey diagram for each bulb to represent the energy transfers. Ⓗ Ⓢ Ⓦ

Ⓓ *The power rating of this toaster is 1100 watts.*

Ⓔ *The power rating of this kettle is 3000 watts.*

7 Look at photos D and E. Ⓗ Ⓢ Ⓦ

  a Which appliance transfers the most electricity each second?

  b Which appliance will cost the most to use for two minutes?

  c Explain your answers to parts **a** and **b**.

8 How much energy does the toaster in photo D transfer every second?

9 a Suggest why people do not always buy the most efficient appliances available. Ⓗ Ⓢ Ⓦ

  b Explain how someone could work out if buying a more efficient appliance will help them to save money in the long run. Ⓗ Ⓢ Ⓦ

I CAN...

○ explain what the power rating of an appliance shows.

○ explain how we can cut electricity bills.

○ explain how this can help the environment. Ⓗ Ⓢ Ⓦ

HowScienceWorks

Can using energy resources be 'green'?

Most scientists agree that burning fossil fuels puts more carbon dioxide into the atmosphere, and that this is making the world warmer. Global warming will affect ecosystems, change weather patterns, and lead to flooding and food shortages. This is not a sustainable use of energy resources. Also, fossil fuels are a non-renewable energy resource, and will run out one day. We need to reduce the amount of carbon dioxide we put into the atmosphere, but what is the best way of doing this?

A

The power industry is working on ways of capturing the CO_2 produced and storing it so that it does not reach the atmosphere.

We should replace some of our power stations with renewable energy resources.

B

Ways of storing carbon dioxide haven't even been tested properly yet! The oil and power companies just want to carry on making money. What we should really do is reduce the amount of electricity we use!

C

HAVE YOUR SAY

What is the best way of reducing the amount of carbon dioxide we put into the atmosphere?

1 Electricity is a way of transferring energy. Write down some other ways in which energy can be transferred.

2 How does using electricity add carbon dioxide to the atmosphere?

3 Give two reasons why burning fossil fuels is not a sustainable way of generating electricity.

4 a What does 'efficiency' mean?
  b Why is it important that we use efficient machines when we can?

HowScienceWorks

The first **artificial satellite** was launched into Earth **orbit** in 1957. Today there are thousands of satellites orbiting the Earth, and even a few orbiting other **planets** in the **Solar System**.

Satellites can be put into different orbits, depending on what they are used for.

Earth observation satellites can be used for:
- weather forecasting.
- making maps.
- scientific research (e.g. finding the temperature of the sea or land).
- spying on other countries to find out where their armies or airfields are.

A *Chris Davis works with satellites.*

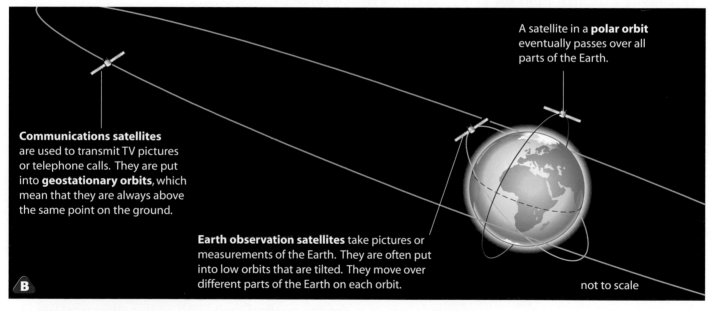

A satellite in a **polar orbit** eventually passes over all parts of the Earth.

Communications satellites are used to transmit TV pictures or telephone calls. They are put into **geostationary orbits**, which mean that they are always above the same point on the ground.

Earth observation satellites take pictures or measurements of the Earth. They are often put into low orbits that are tilted. They move over different parts of the Earth on each orbit.

not to scale

B

1 Why do engineers who design satellites and space probes need to understand gravity? Give as many reasons as you can.

2 Suggest the kinds of things that scientists can find out from:
   a satellites in orbit around the Earth.
   b satellites in orbit around other planets or moons.

3 Why do you think a satellite that transmits TV programmes is put into a geostationary orbit? (*Hint:* think about how the signals get to a TV set.)

4 a How has the use of satellites affected the way people live?
   b Which of these effects are benefits, and which are drawbacks?

What is gravity?

When any two objects are near each other they exert a tiny force that tries to pull them together. This force is called **gravity**. The bigger the **mass** of the object, the stronger the force it exerts.

Even your body attracts things around you by gravity, but the force you exert is too small for you to notice. The Earth has an enormous mass, so it exerts a large force. This force pulls you towards the centre of the Earth.

The hard ground you stand on stops you from sinking any further towards the centre of the Earth. The force of gravity pulling on you is your **weight**, and is measured in **newtons (N)**. Gravity on Earth pulls on every kilogram with a force of 10 N, so in drawing B the boy's weight is 350 N.

A

mass = 90 kg

mass = 35 kg

weight = 350 N

force from floor

force from floor

B *The boy does not have a very big mass, so his weight is not very big. The man has a bigger mass, so he weighs more than the boy.*

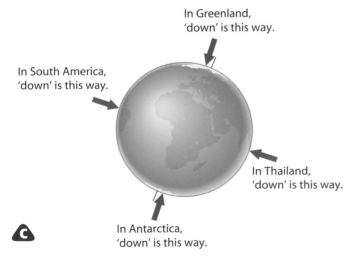

In Greenland, 'down' is this way.

In South America, 'down' is this way.

In Thailand, 'down' is this way.

In Antarctica, 'down' is this way.

C

1 Why is the skydiver in photo A falling towards the Earth?

2 Look at drawing B.
   a What is the man's weight?
   b Why is his weight bigger than the boy's weight?
3 Why is a motorbike heavier than a bicycle?
4 Your weight changes a little during each day. Suggest one reason why your weight might:
   a increase.   b decrease.

Gravity always pulls things towards the centre of the Earth. This is the direction we call 'down'. The actual direction of 'down' depends where on the Earth you are.

5 Copy this diagram, and draw in the direction that the balls will fall. One has been done for you.

Earth

D

Your weight depends on your mass and on the strength of the Earth's gravity. The Moon is smaller than the Earth, so its gravity is less. The Moon's gravity is about one-sixth of the Earth's gravity. If you could go to the Moon your mass would be the same, but your weight would be less.

The strength of gravity between two objects also depends on how far apart the objects are. If you go up a mountain on the Earth you are getting a bit further away from the centre of the Earth, and you will weigh slightly less at the top than you did at the bottom. This effect is very small – if you climbed to the top of Mount Everest you would only weigh about 1 N less than you do now!

The lunar module was carried in this part of the rocket.

F The Saturn V rocket helped to take astronauts to the Moon. Its engines produced a force of 34 000 000 N.

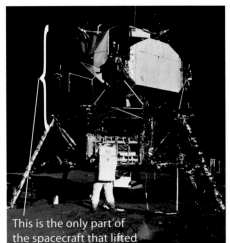

This is the only part of the spacecraft that lifted off from the Moon.

G The lunar module's engine produced a force of 15 000 N.

The unit for force is named after Isaac Newton (1643–1727), who worked out how gravity affects objects. Many scientists in Newton's day thought that gravity was the centre of the Universe pulling on you, and you only got pulled down to Earth because the Earth was between you and the centre of the Universe.

6 Ganymede is the biggest of Jupiter's moons. The mass of Ganymede is twice as big as the mass of our Moon.
   a Would the force of gravity on Ganymede be more or less than the force of gravity on our Moon?
   b Explain your answer.

7 Look at photos F and G. Why did the engines on the Saturn V rocket need to produce so much more force than the engine on the lunar module? (*Hint:* there are two reasons.)

8 The engineers who design spacecraft try to keep the mass as low as possible. Explain why, in as much detail as you can.

9 The gravity on Mars is about 0.4 times the gravity on Earth. Suggest how much force would be needed for a space probe to take off from Mars. Explain how you worked out your answer. **H S W**

I CAN...
○ explain the difference between mass and weight.
○ recall the factors that affect the strength of gravity.

Is there gravity in space?

The Sun is more than 300 000 times more massive than the Earth. Its gravity is very strong. The Earth is moving around the Sun at approximately 100 000 km/h. If there were no gravity from the Sun the Earth would fly off into space. The force of gravity between the Sun and the Earth keeps the Earth moving in an **elliptical** (oval) **orbit** around the Sun.

Gravity gets weaker when the two objects attracting each other are a long way apart. Neptune is 30 times further from the Sun than the Earth is. The force of gravity between the Sun and Neptune is much weaker than between the Sun and the Earth, but it is still strong enough to keep Neptune in its orbit. Neptune takes longer than the Earth to orbit the Sun, and also moves more slowly in its orbit.

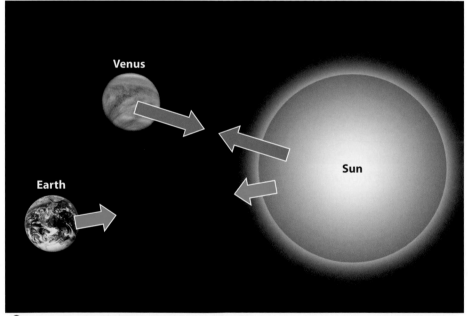

A *The mass of Venus is similar to the mass of the Earth. The force of gravity between Venus and the Sun is about 1.6 times as strong as the force between the Earth and the Sun.*

Anything that orbits a **planet** is called a satellite. The Moon is a **natural satellite** of the Earth. It is much closer to the Earth than the Sun, so it is affected by the Earth's gravity. The Moon is kept in its orbit around the Earth by the gravitational attraction between the Moon and the Earth. Most of the other planets in the **Solar System** also have moons.

1 What stops the Earth from moving away from the Sun?
2 On which planet in the Solar System would the Sun's gravity be strongest? Explain your answer.
3 The force of gravity between the Sun and the Earth is over 80 times as big as the force between the Sun and the Moon. Why is this?

B *This photo of the Moon and the Earth was taken from the Apollo 8 spacecraft while it was orbiting the Moon.*

4 What is a satellite?
5 Why is the Moon called a 'natural' satellite?
6 What kept Apollo 8 in orbit around the Moon?

Artificial satellites can be put into orbit around the Earth, or around other planets or moons. A satellite is kept in its orbit by the gravitational attraction between the satellite and the planet or moon it is orbiting.

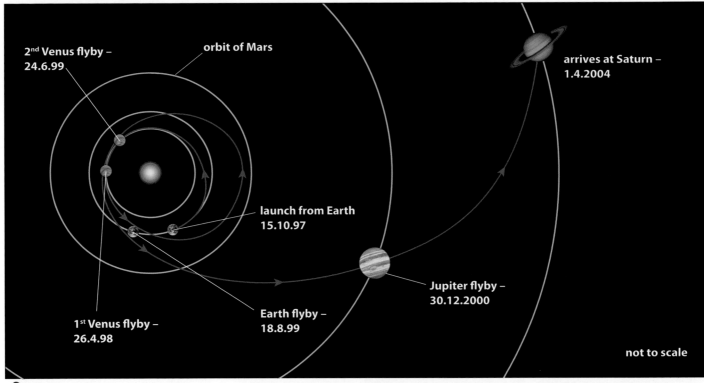

2nd Venus flyby – 24.6.99

orbit of Mars

arrives at Saturn – 1.4.2004

launch from Earth 15.10.97

Jupiter flyby – 30.12.2000

Earth flyby – 18.8.99

1st Venus flyby – 26.4.98

not to scale

C *Engineers planning the route of a spacecraft can use the gravity of other planets to help the spacecraft to reach its destination. This shows how the Cassini* **space probe** *got to Saturn.*

Beyond the Solar System

Gravity does not stop outside the Solar System. There is a force of attraction between all the **stars** in a **galaxy**. This holds the galaxy together. Even different galaxies attract each other. There is a force of gravity everywhere in the **Universe**, although it is very weak in some places.

D *The stars in the Sombrero galaxy are held together by gravity.*

7 What holds all the stars in a galaxy together?

8 Some galaxies are found in groups. What keeps these groups of galaxies together?

I CAN...

○ describe how gravity can affect planets, moons, stars and spacecraft.

How is information gathered by astronomers and space scientists?

HowScienceWorks

Until late in the twentieth century, scientists could only learn about planets and stars using telescopes based on the Earth.

Galileo Galilei (1564–1642) made the first detailed observations of the Solar System with a telescope in 1610. He discovered that there were moons orbiting Jupiter, and published his findings in a book called *Sidereus nuncius* (Latin for 'Starry messenger').

A *Telescopes on Earth are often built on the tops of mountains. These telescopes are at 2600 m in the Atacama Desert in Chile, which is above most of the clouds and dust in the atmosphere. They are run by the European Southern Observatory. Thirteen European countries collaborate to pay for the telescopes, which are used by scientists from those countries.*

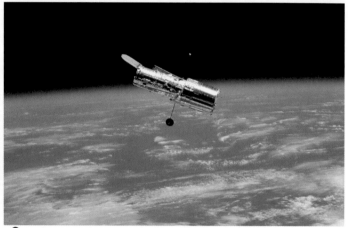

B *The Hubble Space Telescope (HST) is in orbit around the Earth. Photo D on page 119 was taken by the HST. Scientists from all over the world can ask for the HST to make observations to help with their research. The HST was the first instrument to detect which chemicals are in the atmosphere of a planet orbiting another star.*

1 Why are large telescopes built on the tops of mountains?

2 a What are the advantages of having a telescope in space instead of on the Earth?
  b What are the disadvantages?

3 a Suggest how scientists share data with each other today.
  b How do you think this was different in Galileo's time?

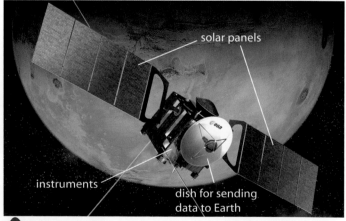

solar panels

instruments

dish for sending data to Earth

C *The European Space Agency **orbiter** Mars Express arrived in orbit around Mars in 2003. It has sent back thousands of images and other information about Mars.*

Scientists have much more information now, from space probes that have flown past or landed on other planets and their moons.

D *The Phoenix **lander** arrived safely on Mars in 2008. It collected samples of the soil and analysed them, and it also sent back other scientific information.*

E *This is the first view of the surface of Titan, one of Saturn's moons. It was sent by the ESA Huygens space probe in 2005.*

Io is one of the moons of Jupiter. **F** *This photo of Io in front of Jupiter was taken by the Hubble Space Telescope in 1997. It shows a volcano erupting on Io (on the left of the moon).*

G *This photo of Io was taken by the Galileo probe in 1997.*

4 The HST could take a much clearer photo of the surface of Mars than its photo of Io (photo F). Why is this?

5 Look at photos F and G.
   a What are the advantages of sending a space probe (rather than using a telescope on Earth) to take photos of a planet or moon?
   b What are the disadvantages?

6 What information could the Phoenix lander obtain that Mars Express cannot?

7 The Apollo astronauts brought back samples of rock from the Moon.
   a Why is this an advantage to scientists?
   b Suggest why this is not done for rock samples from Mars.

8 The HST uses energy from sunlight to make electricity. The Galileo space probe used a nuclear power source. Suggest why the power sources are different.

I CAN...

- describe some different ways in which scientists can find out about the Solar System.
- evaluate the advantages and disadvantages of some of these methods.

How is the electromagnetic spectrum useful in astronomy?

Visible light transfers energy from luminous objects. **Infrared radiation** also transfers energy; we can feel this energy as heat. Visible light and infrared radiation both travel as waves, and are part of a family of waves called the **electromagnetic spectrum**. These waves all travel at the same speed, but have different frequencies and wavelengths.

> **1 a** List the parts of the electromagnetic spectrum in order.
> **b** Write down one use for each part of the spectrum.

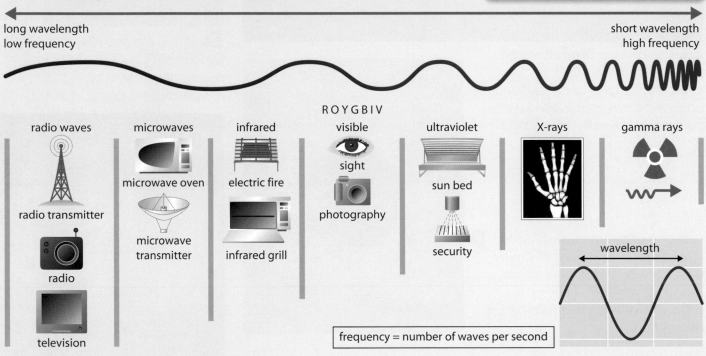

A The waves in the electromagnetic spectrum.

Stars give out radiation in all parts of the electromagnetic spectrum. There are many different kinds of star, and each type gives out different combinations of electromagnetic waves. The electromagnetic radiation given out by a star is evidence for the kinds of nuclear reactions happening inside the star. The Earth's atmosphere absorbs some parts of the electromagnetic spectrum, so some observations have to be made by satellites.

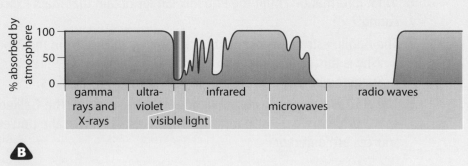

B

2 Which types of electromagnetic radiation can be detected using telescopes on Earth? Explain your answer.

3 Look at photo C. What are the differences between a radio telescope and a telescope that detects visible light?

4 Suggest why the SETI project examines radio waves rather than other parts of the electromagnetic spectrum.

Infrared radiation can pass through dusty regions of space without being scattered, and can also detect some objects that are too cool to be seen using visible light.

C *The National Radio Astronomy Observatory in the USA, which detects radio waves from space.*

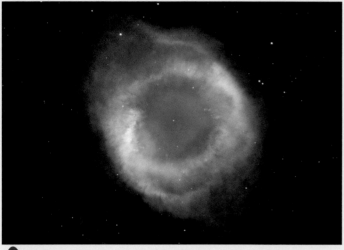

D *This visible light image of the Helix nebula was taken by the HST. It shows the cloud of dust and gas around a dying star.*

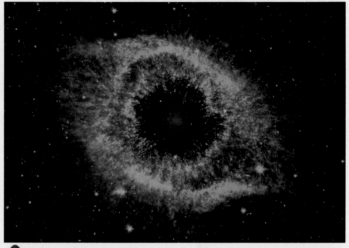

E *This infrared image of the Helix nebula was taken by NASA's Spitzer space telescope.*

F *This picture of galaxy M106 was made from images from four different telescopes. Yellow in the picture represents visible light, red represents infrared, blue represents X-rays, and purple represents radio waves. Two of the 'arms' of the galaxy cannot be seen using visible light. This type of image is called a 'false colour' image.*

!

The Search for Extra-Terrestrial Intelligence (SETI) is a project that analyses radio signals from space to see if any of them might have been sent by intelligent life forms. The SETI@home project allows ordinary people all over the world to help analyse the data using a special screen-saver on their home computers.

5 What are the advantages of using telescopes to detect electromagnetic wavelengths other than visible light?

6 Look at photo F.
   a How many of the telescopes used to provide information for this image must have been on satellites? Explain your answer.
   b What are the advantages of using false colour images?

How did we get our current model of the Solar System?

One of the early models to explain the Solar System was put forward by a Greek thinker called Aristotle (384–322 BCE). He suggested that the Earth did not move, and the Sun, Moon and planets were fixed to solid, transparent spheres that rotated around the Earth.

One way of trying to decide whether or not a model is right is to use it to make predictions. Aristotle's model of the Solar System could be used to predict where the planets would be on a particular date. Unfortunately, it did not always work. Another Greek, called Ptolemy (c.85–165 CE), changed the model so that it made better predictions. However, these predictions were still not very accurate.

> **1** Ptolemy and Aristotle suggested different models of the Solar System.
> **a** Write down one similarity between their models.
> **b** Write down one difference.
> **c** Why don't we use either of these models today?

In 1543, a Polish astronomer called Nicolaus Copernicus (1473–1543) published a book that suggested that the Earth went around the Sun. Copernicus still had complicated little circles for the planets to move around. His model was a little simpler than Ptolemy's, but was still not as accurate as it could be. At that time the Catholic Church believed that the Earth was at the centre of the Universe with everything else moving around it. The heavens were perfect and never-changing. Copernicus was afraid of being punished by the Church for his ideas, so he did not allow his work to be published until he was dying.

HowScienceWorks

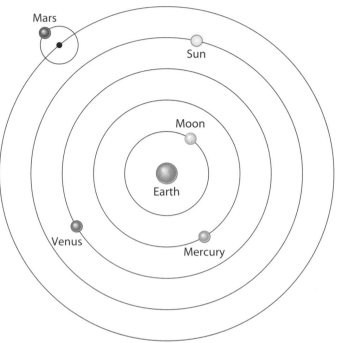

A This is part of Ptolemy's system, which had the Earth in the centre, and some of the planets moving in little circles, which were moving in bigger circles!

B The Italian scientist Galileo Galilei (1564–1642) published a book in 1632 that supported Copernicus' model of the Earth moving around the Sun. The Catholic Church punished him by sentencing him to house arrest for the rest of his life.

It was a long time before everyone accepted that the Sun, not the Earth, was at the centre of the Solar System. There were many reasons for this; one reason was that the model proposed by Copernicus and Galileo was still very complicated and did not make completely accurate predictions.

Our modern model of the Solar System was first suggested by Johannes Kepler (1571–1630) in 1609. He suggested that the planets moved in ellipses, not circles. The model can be used to calculate very accurately where the planets will be at any time, and is used to help spacecraft get to their destinations.

However, scientists also like to know *why* things move in the way they do. This part of the model took a little longer. Several scientists had the idea that there was a force of attraction (called gravity) between all the planets and the Sun, and that this force got weaker as the distance increased. However, it was Sir Isaac Newton (1643–1727) who used this idea to calculate the movements of the planets, and showed that his calculations matched observations made by astronomers.

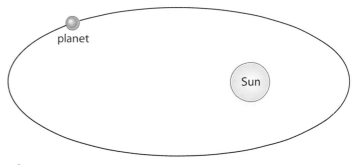

C An elliptical orbit.

D John Flamsteed (1646–1719) provided Newton with many observations to help him to check his model.

2 a What was the main difference between Ptolemy's model and Copernicus' model?
  b Give two reasons why Copernicus' model wasn't accepted by everyone at the time.
  c What evidence did Galileo discover that showed that not everything orbited around the Earth? (*Hint:* You may need to look back at page 120.)
3 What was the main difference between Copernicus' model and Kepler's model?
4 How did Isaac Newton contribute to our current model of the Solar System?
5 Why do we use Kepler's model today?

I CAN...

- describe how ideas about the Solar System have changed.
- recall why new ideas were not always accepted straight away.
- explain why scientists accept our current model.

9Jd Who owns space?

Should anyone be allowed to own parts of space?

On the Earth, a country is usually said to belong to the people who live there, although many wars have been fought because people cannot agree on this.

The Outer Space Treaty was signed in 1969. It prohibits using the Moon or other bodies for military purposes, and prevents any country from claiming to own the Moon. It does not prevent companies from mining or using the Moon for other commercial purposes.

In 1980 the American Dennis Hope registered a claim to the Moon, saying that the Outer Space Treaty does not prevent individuals from owning the Moon. He sells plots of land on the Moon, and allows companies in other countries to sell plots of lunar land. Some companies will even sell you parts of Mars or Venus!

A In 1959, 12 countries signed the Antarctic Treaty, which declared that no one country owned the continent, and did not allow mining and other commercial activities there.

B A certificate of ownership for part of the Moon.

C How long will it be before you could visit your plot of land on the Moon?

HAVE YOUR SAY

Do you think that countries, companies or people should be allowed to own parts of the other planets?

1 You could buy a plot of land on the Moon, on Mars or on Venus. Draw up a table to show the similarities and differences between these three places.

2 a Which of the three bodies in question 1 do we know most about?
  b How has this information been gathered?

3 If we run out of certain materials on Earth, we may be able to get them from other planets.
  a Which of the three bodies in question 1 is most likely to be mined first? Explain your answer in as much detail as you can.
  b Which is likely to be the last one to be mined? Explain your answer.
  c Do you think we should live on other planets and mine them?

4 a Where would you rather have your plot of land: on the Moon, on Mars or on Venus? Explain your answer.
  b Which of these places would you rather visit?

Record breakers

Humans are competitive. We like to win competitions or races if we can, or to be the fastest or the best at something. People can set some speed records by running fast over specific distances, but many speed records involve engineering and technology.

A ThrustSSC *is the world's first* **supersonic** *car – Andy Green travelled faster than the speed of sound when he broke the world land speed record in 1997, travelling at over 1200 km/h (745 mph).*

B *Ken Warby set the current water speed record of 511 km/h in 1978 in the* Spirit of Australia.

C *The Tu-144 holds the record for the fastest passenger aircraft. It could travel at around 2500 km/h. Like most aeroplanes, it has a* **streamlined** *shape to reduce its* **air resistance**.

1 a Sketch *ThrustSSC* and draw labelled arrows to show all the forces on it when it is moving at a steady speed.
 b Sketch the *Spirit of Australia* and draw labelled arrows to show all the forces on it when it is speeding up.
 c Why aren't the forwards and backwards forces the same size in both your drawings?

2 On *ThrustSSC*:
 a how could the forwards force be increased?
 b what would happen if the forwards force was increased?
 c how could the backwards force be increased?
 d what would happen if the backwards force was increased?

3 The land speed record is much faster than the water speed record. Suggest why this is so. Use the word 'resistance' in your answer.

4 A car like *ThrustSSC* has to be very carefully designed. Suggest some of the problems the engineers who designed it had to solve.

How can we work out how fast something is moving?

In a race all the cars set off at the same time, and the one that gets to the finish line in the shortest time wins the race. If you want to work out the **speed** of the winning car, you have to know the distance of the race and the time the winning car took to travel that distance.

You can calculate the speed using this formula:

$$speed = \frac{distance}{time}$$

The units for speed depend on the measurements you make. For instance, if a car travels 250 miles in five hours, its speed would be measured in **miles per hour** (**mph**). Speed is also measured in **metres per second** (**m/s**) and **kilometres per hour** (**km/h**).

A Nigel Mansell set the lap record at Brand's Hatch. He completed the 3703 metre circuit in 69.59 seconds.

$$speed = \frac{3703\,m}{69.59\,s} \quad or \quad speed = 3703\,m \div 69.59\,s$$

$$= 53.21 \text{ metres per second (m/s)}$$

1 How fast is the car going?

A racing car has to slow down to go round the bends, and it may have a pit stop to refuel. It travels fastest on the straight sections of the track. The speed of the car worked out from the total distance and the time taken is called the **mean speed** (or average speed) for the race.

2 Was Nigel Mansell's fastest speed at Brand's Hatch higher or lower than 53.21 m/s? Explain your answer.

B A pit stop.

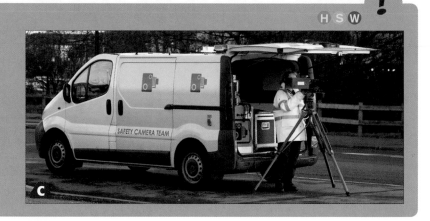

There are thousands of speed cameras on Britain's roads. These use radar or sensors in the road to detect speeding cars. They also take photographs of speeding cars to identify them.

C

Sometimes we know the speed that something is travelling at, and want to know how far it will travel in a certain time, or how long it will take to go a certain distance. We can rearrange the formula for speed to give these equations:

distance = speed × time

$$time = \frac{distance}{speed}$$

You can remember these formulae by remembering this triangle:

d = distance travelled
s = mean speed
t = time taken

D

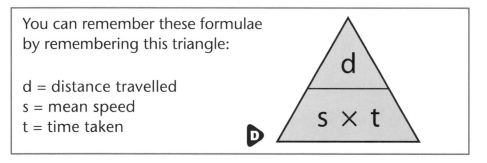

H S W

How could you work out the speed of toy cars going down a ramp? Write a plan for your investigation.
- Does the slope of the ramp make a difference to the speed?
- Does the mass of the car make a difference?
- Is the speed the same all the way down the ramp?
- How will you measure the speed?

3 Write down three different units that are usually used for speed.

4 The TGV train takes two hours to travel the 400 km route between Paris and Lyon.
  a What is the mean speed of the TGV between Paris and Lyon?
  b The top speed of the TGV in normal service is 515 km/h. How long would it take to go from Paris to Lyon at this speed?
  c Why does the journey take longer than your answer to part **b**? Explain in as much detail as you can.

5 Family cars can now travel faster than some of the early racing cars. How has faster travel changed the way people behave? **H S W**

6 Look at photo C. The speed camera has to provide accurate and reliable data. **H S W**
  a Explain what 'accurate' and 'reliable' mean.
  b Why do the data have to be accurate and reliable?

I CAN...

- recall different units for speed.
- recall and use the formula for calculating speed.
- explain what mean speed is.
- explain how measuring speed is important for road safety. **H S W**

How do forces change the speed?

The Helios space probe was launched in 1976 to gather information about the Sun, but it is no longer sending information back to the Earth. There are no friction forces in space to slow it down, so it will continue to orbit the Sun.

If there are no forces on something that is moving, it will carry on moving at the same speed. On Earth it is impossible to find something with no forces on it at all. Moving objects usually have **air resistance** or **friction** acting on them.

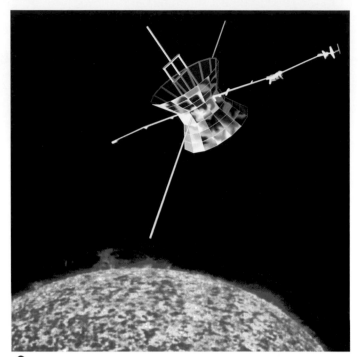

A *The Helios 2 space probe is the fastest human-made object. It reaches a speed of over 250 000 km/h during part of its orbit around the Sun.*

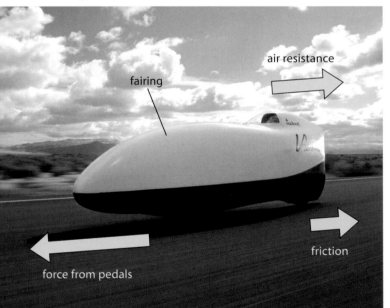

fairing

air resistance

friction

force from pedals

B *Sam Whittingham holds the record for the fastest human-powered vehicle. He reached a speed of over 130 km/h.*

The record for the longest distance cycled in one hour on a standard, upright bicycle stands at 49.7 km. Records like this are often attempted at high altitudes where the thinner air creates less air resistance.

The bicycle in photo B is moving at a constant speed. The forwards force from the pedals is the same size as the total force from air resistance and friction. The forces are balanced. **Balanced forces** cannot make something start or stop moving, or change its speed. If something is already moving, balanced forces keep it moving at the same speed.

1 Why doesn't the Helios probe need a force to keep it moving?
2 Why does Sam need to keep pedalling to keep his bicycle moving at a constant speed?
3 a Write down the differences between Sam's bicycle and a normal bicycle.
  b Why do you think Sam's bicycle has these differences?

If the forces on something are **unbalanced**, it will change speed or change the direction it is moving in. The forward force on this motorbike is much bigger than the forces of friction and air resistance. The motorbike is **accelerating** (speeding up).

C

> **4** Are the forces balanced or unbalanced when:
>   **a** a car is starting off from traffic lights?
>   **b** a car travels at a steady speed?
>   **c** a car slows down at a junction?
> **5 a** What are the forces on the vase?
>   **b** Are they balanced or unbalanced?
>
>
>
> D

Almost everything has at least two forces acting on it, and often more. For example, the motorbike in photo C also has weight and a force from the ground on it. We can ignore these forces if we are thinking about the speed of the motorbike along the track. They are at right angles to the direction in which the bike is moving, so they do not have any effect on its horizontal speed.

If the forces on something are unbalanced, we can work out the **resultant force**. This is the difference between the total forces in one direction and the total forces in the opposite direction.

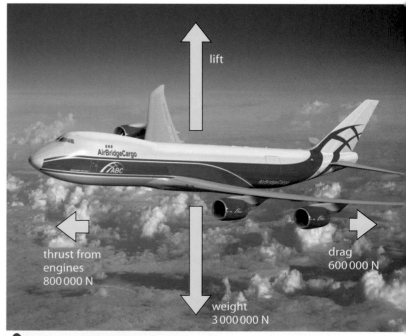

E *The resultant horizontal force on the airliner is 200 000 N in a forwards direction.*

> **6** Look at photo E.
>   **a** What will happen to the speed of the aeroplane? Explain your answer.
>   **b** The aeroplane is not moving upwards or downwards. What is the size of the lift force? Explain how you worked out your answer.

I CAN...

○ explain what balanced and unbalanced forces do to the movement of an object.
○ explain what a resultant force is.

How do we work out the acceleration?

If there are unbalanced forces on something, its speed will change. A change in speed is an acceleration. The units for speed are metres per second or m/s. Acceleration is the change in speed every second, so the units are metres/second/second (written as **m/s/s**). If something changes its speed by 5 m/s every second, its acceleration is 5 m/s/s.

$$\text{acceleration} = \frac{\text{change in speed}}{\text{time}}$$

A The SSC Aero is the world's fastest production car. It can go from 0 to 60 mph (0–26.8 m/s) in only 2.78 seconds.

1 What is the maximum acceleration of the SSC Aero car?

The acceleration depends on:
• the size of the force.
• the mass of the object.
If the same force is applied, a smaller mass will accelerate faster than a bigger mass.

B

If the masses are the same, a big force will produce a bigger acceleration than a small force.

2 Why can motorbikes usually accelerate much faster than cars, even though they have smaller engines?

C

You can calculate acceleration using this formula:

$$\text{acceleration} = \frac{\text{force}}{\text{mass}}$$

H S W

How would you find out what affects acceleration?
○ What difference does the size of the force make?
○ Does the mass of the trolley make any difference?
○ How will you measure the acceleration?

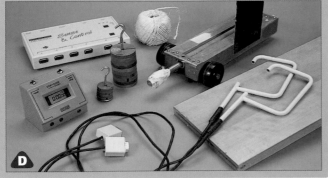

D

3 A jet fighter has a mass at take-off of 28 000 kg.
  a Its engines produce a force of 70 000 N. What is its acceleration?
  b What is its acceleration if the force from the engine is increased to 120 000 N?

Sometimes we know the acceleration of a vehicle and want to know its mass, or the size of the force from its engine. We can rearrange the formula for acceleration to give these equations:

force = mass × acceleration

$$\text{mass} = \frac{\text{force}}{\text{acceleration}}$$

E A drag-racing track is normally ¼ mile long (approximately 400m). The car with the best acceleration wins the race.

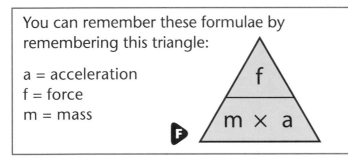

You can remember these formulae by remembering this triangle:

a = acceleration
f = force
m = mass

F

Something slowing down is **decelerating**. The force from the brakes makes a car decelerate. Cars also decelerate very suddenly in a crash. Cars are designed with safety systems to make the deceleration on the passengers less, which reduces the number of injuries.

4 Make up a mnemonic to help you to remember the formula for calculating acceleration.

5 A drag racer accelerates at 30 m/s/s. Its mass is 950 kg. What force does its engine produce?

6 The engine of the car in photo A produces a maximum force of 12 000 N. What mass does the car have?

7 Look at photo G. **H S W**
  a Why do you think the bonnet is designed to crumple?
  b List some other safety features that modern cars have.

8 One car comes to a stop in a much shorter time than another car. Think of as many reasons for this statement as you can.

G The bonnet of the car is designed to crumple when it hits something.

I CAN...

- explain what acceleration is.
- use a formula to calculate acceleration.
- describe how force and mass affect acceleration.
- describe how ideas about changing speed are important for road safety. **H S W**

Why do things have a top speed?

Cars, trains and aeroplanes all have a top speed. The top speed of any vehicle depends on the force that its engine can produce, and on the **drag** forces caused by air resistance.

People have a top speed too. Skydivers do not have engines, but their weight pulls them downwards.

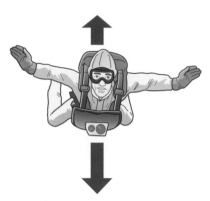

A *When the skydiver first jumps out of the plane he is not moving very fast. His weight is a bigger force than the air resistance, so he will accelerate (go faster) downwards.*

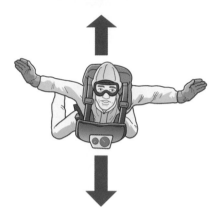

B *As he gets faster, the air resistance increases because there are more air particles hitting him every second. His weight is still bigger than the air resistance, so he will carry on getting faster.*

C *Eventually his air resistance has increased so much that it is the same size as his weight. The forces on him are balanced, so he will not go any faster. The speed he is going is his top speed, or* **terminal velocity**.

D *When he opens his parachute, his air resistance suddenly increases. The upwards force is now much bigger than the downwards force, so he slows down.*

E *As he slows down, the air resistance from the parachute gets less, until it is the same size as his weight. He stops slowing down, and carries on falling at a constant speed. This is a new terminal velocity.*

1 Look at pictures A to E.
  a Which pictures show balanced forces?
  b Which pictures show the skydiver accelerating?
  c Which picture shows the skydiver slowing down?
  d Why is the force of air resistance bigger in C than it is in A?

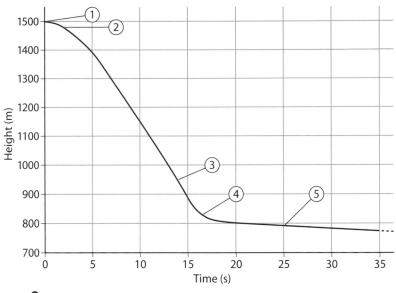

How could you investigate the factors that affect the air resistance of a parachute?
- What could you change?
- How could you measure the air resistance?

You can show what happens during a skydive using a **distance–time graph**. The steeper the line, the faster the skydiver is falling.

- At point 1 on graph F the skydiver has just jumped out of the plane.
- At point 2 he is moving downwards at about 40 m/s. His air resistance is increasing, but it is still smaller than his weight. He is still gaining speed.

F *Distance–time graph for a skydiver.*

2 Describe what is happening at each of points 3 to 5 on graph F. For each position, describe the size of the forces, what is happening to the skydiver, and how his speed is changing.

3 Compare these skydivers to the one in picture A. Which one will have the highest terminal velocity? Explain your answer.

In October 1797, Andre-Jacques Garnerin became the first human to descend from a balloon using a parachute. He jumped from 900 metres. The highest parachute jump ever made was by Captain Joseph Kittinger in 1960. He jumped from 31 300 metres, and needed a special suit to allow him to breathe.

4 The engineers designing a new car estimate that its top speed will be 90 mph. Describe two ways in which they could increase its top speed, and explain why each method will work. **H S W**

I CAN...

- recall how air resistance changes with speed.
- use ideas about balanced forces to explain why things have a terminal velocity.
- interpret information from a distance–time graph. **H S W**

How do engineers design faster vehicles?

The land speed record has been broken many times since it was first set in 1898. In 1983 the Englishman Richard Noble broke the record in *Thrust2*, achieving a speed of 1019 km/h.

In 1992 Noble met Ron Ayres, an **aerodynamicist**, who agreed to work on a design for a new car. Noble didn't just want to beat his old record, he also wanted to go faster than the speed of sound.

Ayres designed a streamlined shape that he thought would be steerable at very high speeds. However, they had to be sure that the design would work and would be safe – high speed cars can flip over if they hit a bump and the way the air flows around a moving vehicle changes as it gets close to the speed of sound. They used **computer modelling** to predict the way that air would flow over the car.

The computer model they used was developed for designing aeroplanes, and had not been used for a car before. The ground beneath the car affects the way that air flows over the car, so they had to make sure the model was making accurate predictions. They put a scale model of the car on a rocket-powered sled which ran at speeds of up to 1300 km/h. Pressure sensors on the model recorded information during each run. This data agreed very closely with the predictions made by the computer model.

How **S**cience **W**orks

A Thrust2.

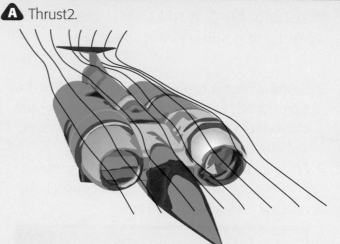

B *A computer model of ThrustSSC.*

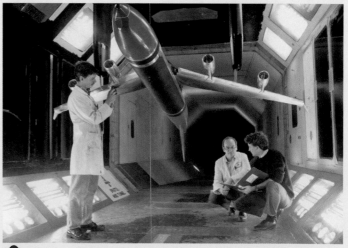

C *Scale models of aeroplanes are tested in wind tunnels to check how accurate computer models are. The wind tunnel blows air past the model, which is fitted with sensors to measure the forces on it and the air pressure around it.*

In 1996 *ThrustSSC* was ready for some test runs, which were carried out in a desert in Jordan. The car was driven by Andy Green, an RAF pilot. The test runs tried out the engines, the brakes and all the control and safety systems in the car. These tests showed that some modifications were needed. In 1997 the team went back to Jordan for final testing.

In 2008 Richard Noble announced a new record-breaking project, this time to reach a speed of 1000 mph! The new car will be called *Bloodhound SSC*. The car will be powered by a jet engine and a rocket. Many of the people from the *ThrustSSC* team are working on the *Bloodhound* project. Ron Ayres worked on the design of the car, and the project is named after the Bloodhound missile, which was one of the first things that Ron worked on in his engineering career.

Richard Noble hopes that, in addition to setting a new record, the Bloodhound project will get more people interested in careers in engineering. He believes that the UK needs more engineers to help to design and build new, efficient vehicles and other machines to reduce our use of fossil fuels.

The actual record attempt was made in the Black Rock Desert in the USA – and they achieved their target of reaching supersonic speeds on October 15, 1997.

D *Just some of the successful* ThrustSSC *team.*

E *Richard Noble and Andy Green (the driver) with a model of* Bloodhound SSC.

1 To set an official record, a car has to make the same run twice (once in each direction) within a certain time. Suggest why this is so.

2 The speed of the car is measured over a set distance. The car does not start at the beginning of the measured distance, but some way before the start. Suggest why.

3 Why do you think the testing and the record attempts were made in deserts? Give as many reasons as you can.

4 Why was a model of *ThrustSSC* tested on a rocket-powered sled?

5 Although *ThrustSSC* was a single vehicle designed for one task, the process of designing it was similar to designing a new car or a new aircraft. Draw a flowchart to show the process used in developing *ThrustSSC*.

6 Suggest some differences between the process for *ThrustSSC* and the process of developing:
   a a new family car to be sold to the public.
   b a new fighter aircraft.

HowScienceWorks

Should people be allowed to risk their lives to break speed records?

Donald Campbell broke both the water speed record and the land speed record many times. Campbell already held the water speed record, at 441 km/h, when he tried to beat his own record in 1967.

A In 1967, Bluebird K7 *flipped over on Campbell's second run and sank into Coniston Water. Campbell was killed instantly.*

B *Divers could not find Campbell's body at the time of the accident. Bluebird was finally recovered in 2001, together with Campbell's body.*

C *Ayrton Senna died in a Formula 1 race in 1994.*

July 1983

TWO RIDERS DIE AT SILVERSTONE

Today's Motorcycle Grand Prix race ended in tragedy for two young riders

March 2001

Formula 1 marshal killed

This is the second death of a race official in six months

D

HAVE YOUR SAY

Many people enjoy watching motor racing, and the website for Richard Noble's *ThrustSSC* record attempt logged over 59 million hits. But should people be allowed to risk their lives to race cars or to set speed records?

1 a What are the forces on a car when it is travelling at a steady speed?
  b How are the forces different at the beginning of a race?
2 a How is the 'mean speed' for a race worked out?
  b Why is the mean speed less than the greatest speed that a car achieved during a race?
3 Why do racing cars have streamlined shapes? Explain in as much detail as you can.
4 What could a designer do to give a car a high acceleration?

Dam it!

We need water to drink, to grow our food and to generate electricity. Water can also be harmful – floods can kill people and animals, destroy houses and damage farmland. **Dams** are one way of trying to control water to prevent damage and to make more water available for our use.

A A modern bridge built across the Grand Anicut (or Kallanai) dam, in Tamil Nadu, India. This is one of the oldest dams still in use. It was constructed from stone about 1900 years ago, to divert waters from the Cauvery river to use for irrigation.

B The Three Gorges Dam, in China, under construction. When it is fully operational it will be the world's largest **hydroelectricity** power station, producing over 18 000 MW of electricity. It will also help to control flooding on the Yangtze River.

C Levees are banks of earth along riverbanks, designed to stop the river flooding the nearby land. Many of the levees in New Orleans broke when Hurricane Katrina hit the city in 2005, and hundreds of people died as a result of the floods.

> **!**
>
> The world's largest reservoir is Lake Volta, in Ghana. It was created when the Akosombo Dam was completed in 1965, and covers an area of 8 500 km². The hydroelectricity power station provides over half of Ghana's electricity.

1 Write down three different reasons why a dam may be built.

2 Look at photo B. Suggest some practical problems that may have to be overcome when building a dam.

3 What kinds of tools or equipment may be needed to build a dam and what would they be used for?

How can we work out the pressure under something?

The bulldozer in photo A has caterpillar tracks. The tracks spread the weight of the bulldozer over a large area, and stop the bulldozer from sinking into the loose earth. The tracks reduce the **pressure** under the bulldozer.

Pressure is the amount of *force* pushing on a certain *area*. The size of the pressure depends on the size of the force, and the size of the area it is pushing on.
- The bigger the force, the bigger the pressure.
- The bigger the area, the smaller the pressure.

A This bulldozer is rebuilding a levee in New Orleans to prevent further flooding.

---

1 Why do bulldozers have caterpillar tracks?
2 Write down three things where: Ⓗ Ⓢ Ⓦ
  a high pressure is useful.
  b low pressure is useful.

Sometimes a high pressure can be useful. The point of a nail has a very small area, so there is a high pressure under it when the nail is hammered. The high pressure helps the nail to go into the wood.

We use this formula to calculate pressure.

$$\text{pressure} = \frac{\text{force}}{\text{area}}$$

It can be written out as a triangle.

f = force
p = pressure
a = area

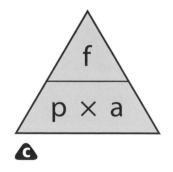

C

Force is measured in newtons, and the area is measured in square metres. So pressure is measured in newtons per square metre (N/m^2). This unit is also called a **pascal** (Pa). 1 Pa = 1 N/m^2.

If the area being measured is small you can measure it in square centimetres (cm^2). The unit of pressure will then be N/cm^2.

To work out how much pressure is put on the ground by the woman in shoes:

pressure = force ÷ area
$$= 600\,\text{N} \div 150\,\text{cm}^2$$
$$= 4\,\text{N/cm}^2$$

area of shoes
150 cm^2

area of boots
360 cm^2

D

Compare the highest and lowest pressure that your weight will put on different parts of your body. You need to:
○ weigh yourself in newtons.
○ measure the area of a part of the body you can balance on (e.g. head, feet, tiptoes, hands).

E

Cars often have reinforcement to protect the driver and passengers if there is an accident. Firemen sometimes need to cut people out of cars after a crash. This new 'super cutter' delivers a pressure of over 500 million N/m^2 at the jaws. The cutter can even cut through the extra reinforcement that expensive cars have for safety.

F

3 Look at drawing D. How much pressure is put on the ground by the woman's boots?

4 A hippopotamus has a mass of 3 tonnes (3000 kg). His four feet cover an area of 0.5 m^2 in total.
  a What does the hippo weigh? (*Hint:* 1 kg has a weight of 10 N.)
  b What is his pressure on the ground?

5 The force produced by the cutter in photo F is 1000 kN. What area of the blades is in contact with a car when it is cutting?

I CAN...
○ recall examples of pressures being changed in the real world. (H)(S) w
○ recall the units for pressure.
○ calculate a pressure.

How do fluids exert pressure?

Everything is made up of tiny particles. In **fluids** (liquids and gases) the particles are moving around in all directions. As they move they bump into each other and any surfaces they come into contact with. The force of the particles hitting things causes pressure. Pressure in liquids and gases comes from all directions.

> **Atmospheric pressure** is about 100 000 Pa, although it changes slightly from day to day. That is like having a mass of one kilogram resting on every square centimetre of your skin. You don't notice the pressure because the fluids inside your body are at a similar pressure.

When you pump up a bicycle tyre you put more air inside it. The particles in a gas are a long way apart, so they can be squashed closer together. When a gas is squashed we say that it is **compressed**. When you push more air into the tyre, the pressure increases because more particles hit the wall of the tyre each second.

Tyres with air inside are called **pneumatic tyres** (from the Greek word for breathe). When a tyre is squashed the air pressure inside gets higher, so the air inside pushes back and the tyre springs back to its original shape if it can.

A Particles in the atmosphere are moving in all directions. The pressure on you is equal in all directions.

1 What is atmospheric pressure in N/m²?

2 a What is a pneumatic tyre?
  b Give two examples of vehicles that have pneumatic tyres.
  c Why is the pressure inside a pneumatic tyre higher than the pressure outside it?

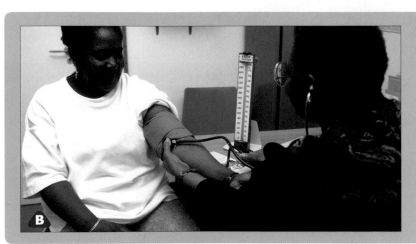

B

A manometer is a U-shaped tube filled with a liquid. The one in the photograph is being used to measure blood pressure. Manometers can also be used to measure gas pressures. Does the kind of liquid in the manometer make any difference to the reading?
- Which variables could affect your choice of liquid to use in a manometer?
- Does the thickness of the tubes matter?

The pressure of the air is due to the weight of the air above us. If we go up a mountain there is less air above us and so the pressure gets less. There are fewer particles in each cubic metre of air.

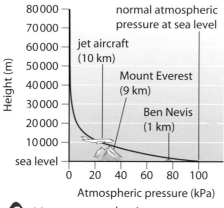

C How atmospheric pressure changes with height above sea level.

D This photo was taken at a height of 2413 m.

E This is the same packet of crisps at sea level.

3 Use ideas about particles to explain why there is less pressure on you from the air if you go up a high mountain. **H S W**

4 Look at photos D and E. Explain why the bag looks different in the two photos, using ideas about particles and pressure. **H S W**

Pressure in water increases as you go deeper. It acts in all directions.

F The arrows represent the force on each square metre.

5 Look at diagram F. Suggest why the dam is built much thicker at the bottom than at the top. **H S W**

6 Look at photo G. Explain why the bottle holding the liquid has to be held above the patient. **H S W**

7 Scientists who capture fish from depths of 1000 m or more for study have to bring them to the surface in pressurised containers. Suggest why they do this. **H S W**

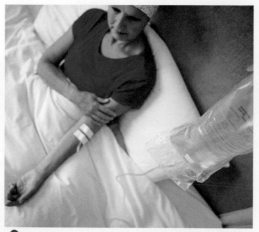

G This woman is attached to a 'drip', which adds a liquid slowly to her blood.

I CAN...

o describe how pressure changes with depth or height.

o explain how pressure influences the way in which some things are designed or used. **H S w**

How can changes in pressure affect humans?

HowScienceWorks

If civil engineers are building a dam or a bridge across a river, the first thing they need to do is to make a dry space to work. Today this is usually done by first building a 'cofferdam', and pumping the water out.

However, this is not the only way to provide dry working space at the bottom of a river or lake. In 1839 Jaques Triger (1801–1867) invented the '**caisson**'. Drawing B shows a caisson being used to build the supports for the Brooklyn Bridge, in New York, in the 1870s.

cofferdam

A Cofferdam keeping water out while the foundations for new buildings are constructed.

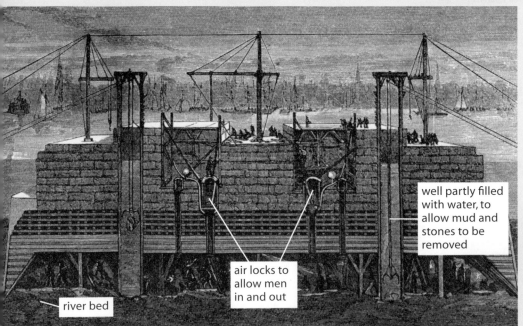

well partly filled with water, to allow mud and stones to be removed

air locks to allow men in and out

river bed

B The caisson was made of wood, and towed into position. Stone was piled on top until it sank to the sea bed. Compressed air was used to force the water out from beneath the caisson.

Le Petit Parisien
Supplément Littéraire Illustré

TRAVAUX DU METROPOLITAIN — AU CHANTIER DE LA CITÉ
Les Ouvriers retrouvent les Cadavres de leurs Camarades victimes du terrible accident

C An accident in a caisson.

People working in caissons sometimes complained of muscular pains after they left the caisson. In some cases men were permanently injured, or died. The condition became known as **caisson disease**. It was sometimes also called the **bends**, because the pain caused people to bend over.

There were different theories about the causes of this sickness. In 1847 a study of men working in compressed air at Lourdes in France reported that the symptoms seen when they left the compressed air could be relieved by recompressing the victim and then decompressing them slowly. However, there was no general agreement about this. On the Brooklyn Bridge project for instance, the inside of the caisson was heated by steam because it was thought that caisson sickness might be due to working in cold conditions.

Felix Hoppe-Seyler (1825–1895) was a German doctor. He carried out experiments similar to Boyle's, and concluded that caisson disease was caused by the sudden release of gases inside the body. In 1889 it became possible to treat caisson diseases using a 'medical lock', which allowed slow decompression.

Caisson disease is now called **decompression sickness**. The current explanation for it is that when we are on land, the pressure inside our bodies is equal to the pressure outside our bodies. If someone is breathing air at a higher than normal pressure, during a dive or because they are working in a caisson, more of the gases in the higher pressure air can dissolve in their blood. If the pressure is reduced too quickly when the diver comes to the surface or the worker leaves the caisson, the dissolved gases are released as bubbles in their blood. The bubbles increase in size as the pressure decreases, and can block blood vessels.

Robert Boyle (1627–1691) was the first person to investigate the effects of decompression on living things. In 1670 he used an air pump to decompress a snake. He observed gas bubbles forming in its eye.

1 In what circumstances can someone suffer from decompression sickness?

2 Why do the following people sometimes suffer from decompression sickness?
   a construction workers
   b divers

3 a Give two alternative theories that were put forward as the cause of decompression sickness.
   b Which theory do scientists now think is correct? Give reasons for your answer.

4 How is decompression sickness treated?

5 How do divers stop themselves getting the bends?

D Divers can avoid decompression sickness by coming up slowly. The longer they have been underwater, and the deeper they have been, the more time they must take coming to the surface. Divers use decompression tables to work out how long they must stop at certain depths to stop bubbles forming in their blood.

How can we use pressure in fluids?

A machine is something that makes work easier by changing the size of a force, or by changing the distance it moves. Many modern machines use liquids to change the size of a force.

Liquids cannot be compressed because there are no gaps between the particles. So liquids can be used to send forces from one place to another. A system which uses liquids like this is called a **hydraulic system**. Hydraulic systems can be used to increase the size of a force.

A Moving earth for dams or railway cuttings is much easier and faster with the help of machines. This steam-powered excavator was used to build a railway in the USA in 1906. It used levers and pulleys to move the digging bucket. Modern excavators use liquids to move digging buckets.

Piston X puts a pressure on the liquid.

$$\text{pressure} = \frac{\text{force}}{\text{area}}$$
$$= 10\,\text{N}/10\,\text{cm}^2$$
$$= 1\,\text{N/cm}^2$$

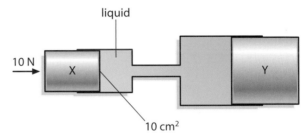

B A **hydraulic press**.

The pressure is the same everywhere in the liquid, so the pressure on piston Y is also $1\,\text{N/cm}^2$. The area of Y is $20\,\text{cm}^2$. We can rearrange the pressure equation to let us calculate the force on Y.

$$\text{force} = \text{pressure} \times \text{area}$$
$$= 1\,\text{N/cm}^2 \times 20\,\text{cm}^2$$
$$\text{force at Y} = 20\,\text{N}$$

We have not got something for nothing. The large force on Y only moves half of the distance of X, so the energy we get out is the same as the energy we put in.

The hydraulic press, as shown in figure B, was invented by the English inventor, Joseph Bramah (1748–1841). He was granted a patent for his invention in 1795.

1 Why can't a liquid be compressed? Ⓗ Ⓢ Ⓦ
2 What is a hydraulic system?
3 Why does the force on Y only move half the original distance? (*Hint:* think about the amount of liquid).

Modern excavators and car brakes use hydraulic systems.

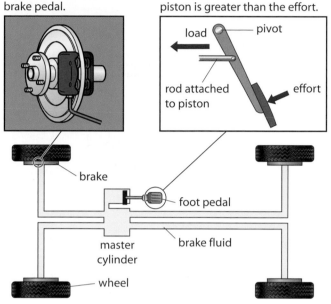

The brake pads do not have to move very far to be pushed against the wheel. The pistons at the brakes are bigger than the piston attached to the brake pedal.

The brake pedal is a lever. It is a **force-multiplier** because the force on the piston is greater than the effort.

load — pivot

rod attached to piston — effort

brake

foot pedal

master cylinder — brake fluid

wheel

C *A car braking system. The pipes carrying the hydraulic fluid do not have to be straight, so they can be made to fit the underneath of the car.*

effort (from hydraulics system)

lever

pivot

load (moves bucket)

D *There are lots of different levers in an excavating machine.*

4 Describe two ways in which the braking system in diagram C magnifies the force from the person's foot.

5 Look at diagram B.
   a What would the force at Y be if the area of Y was $30\,cm^2$?
   b How far would Y move?
   c What would the force at Y be if the area of Y was $5\,cm^2$?
   d How far would Y move?

6 A car's brakes do not work properly if air gets into the pipes. Explain why this is so, using ideas about particles. Ⓗ Ⓢ Ⓦ

7 Look at photo D. The labelled lever is moved by a hydraulic piston.
   a Is the lever a force-multiplier or a **distance multiplier**? (*Hint:* how far does the bucket move compared to the end where the effort is applied?)
   b Give two reasons why the piston providing the effort needs to provide a very large force.

8 Look at photos A and D.
   a What are the differences between the two machines?
   b What advantages does the modern machine have compared to the 1906 machine?

I CAN...

- explain why liquids are used in hydraulic systems. Ⓗ Ⓢ w
- describe how a hydraulic press works.
- calculate the force produced by a hydraulic system.

How do things balance?

The tower crane is lifting a large weight. The weight is producing a turning force in one direction, and this is balanced by the turning force caused by the weight of the counterweight. The **turning effect** of a force is called a **moment**.

The size of the moment depends on the size of the force, and the distance between the force and the **pivot**. Moments are measured in units called **newton metres (N m)**.

We use this formula to calculate moments:

moment of the force (N m) = **force (N)** × **perpendicular distance from the pivot (m)**

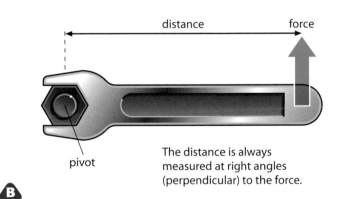

distance   force

The distance is always measured at right angles (perpendicular) to the force.

pivot

B

A This tower crane is lifting steel girders to the top of the building. The **counterweights** help to stop it falling over.

counterweights   jib   sliding pulley block

10 N

30 cm

C

The woman in drawing C is tightening a nut with a wrench. She is holding it 30 cm from the nut and putting a 10 N force on it.

distance from the pivot = 30 cm = 0.3 m
moment = force × distance
= 10 N × 0.3 m
= 3 N m

1 What is the name for the turning effect of a force?

2 A mechanic applies a force of 50 N at a distance of 40 cm from the pivot on a wheel wrench. What is the size of the moment?

3 A plumber uses a spanner on a tap. She puts a force of 100 N on the spanner 15 cm from the tap. What is the size of the moment?

How many different ways can you arrange the masses to balance?
● Can you work out a rule for making them balance?

anticlockwise moment caused by force on sails

clockwise moment caused by weight of crew

E *The boat stays at the same angle because the clockwise moment is the same as the anticlockwise moment.*

When an object is balanced, the clockwise and anticlockwise moments are the same. The object is **in equilibrium**.

4 Look at photo E.
The force on the sail is caused by the wind. What will happen if the wind drops?

5 Give two other examples of objects in equilibrium because the moments are balanced.

6 a Calculate the clockwise and anticlockwise moments on this crane.
  b If the distance of the left-hand load is reduced to 20 m from the tower, what is the maximum load that can be lifted?

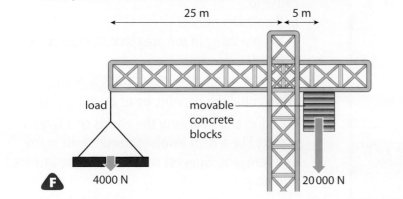

25 m   5 m

load

movable concrete blocks

F   4000 N   20 000 N

I CAN...

● calculate the moment of a force.
● explain how to use moments to work out if something will balance.

HowScience**W**orks

How should we decide whether to build a new dam?

Building a dam costs a lot of money, and results in loss of habitats and removal of people in the area covered by the reservoir. Sometimes these losses are outweighed by the gains, if the dam produces clean hydroelectricity, or prevents damage caused by flooding further downstream.

The World Bank provides loans to developing countries to help them to develop their industries and reduce poverty. The money they lend is often spent on big projects. One very controversial project is the Bujagali dam in Uganda.

> The new dam would allow Uganda to generate more hydroelectricity. We will be able to sell some electricity to Kenya, which will help our economy and provide money for schools and hospitals.

A

> Most people in Uganda are not connected to the electricity grid. This new dam will not help them. If the country is going to get into debt from loans like this, the money would be better spent on lots of small projects that will help local communities.

C

> The Bujagali Falls would be covered by the reservoir. We earn money from tourists who come to see this beautiful place, and go rafting. The Falls are also important to the local people.

B

> The dam that is already on this river is affecting the water in Lake Victoria, which is very important for wildlife. This new dam will just make it worse. And if global warming reduces the rainfall, which is possible, we won't even get the electricity they are promising!

D

HAVE YOUR SAY

Should the Bujagali dam be built?
- What needs to be considered when deciding whether or not to carry out a big project like a new dam?
- What other information do you need to find out to give a better answer?
- What criteria will you use in selecting your information? How will using criteria help you?

1 What problems do you think a large dam could cause to:
   a the environment?
   b people living in the area that the reservoir will flood?
   c people living downstream of the dam?
2 What could the benefits be of building a dam?
3 Planning and assessing the effects of a large project like a dam involves people with many different jobs. Suggest who needs to be involved and why.

How to use the Refresher Units

Pages 152-181 refresh some the main ideas covered in this course. You may have forgotten something from your work earlier in the course, or you may still be confused about something. The Refresher Units will help you.

If you need help remembering something from the course, have a look at the relevant section in these Refresher Units to help you.
To find what you need:
- flick through pages 152-181
- look up a key word in the index (pages 191-192)

In the ActiveBook, clicking on this icon will download a word version of the Refresher Unit spread, which you can then edit.

P and the red band indicate things covered in Units I – L in each book. C and a blue band indicate Units E – H, and B and a green band indicate Units A – D.

Each spread has a clear title stating what topics are covered.

Each spread is divided into sections, which all have a simple title telling you what that section is about.

A lot of the explanations are in the form of drawings to make recapping quick and easy.

This tab tells you in which unit this work was covered. In the ActiveBook, clicking on this tab will download the Summary Sheet from that unit. You can then edit the Summary Sheet.

Key words are all in bold.

Key equations and formulae are highlighted.

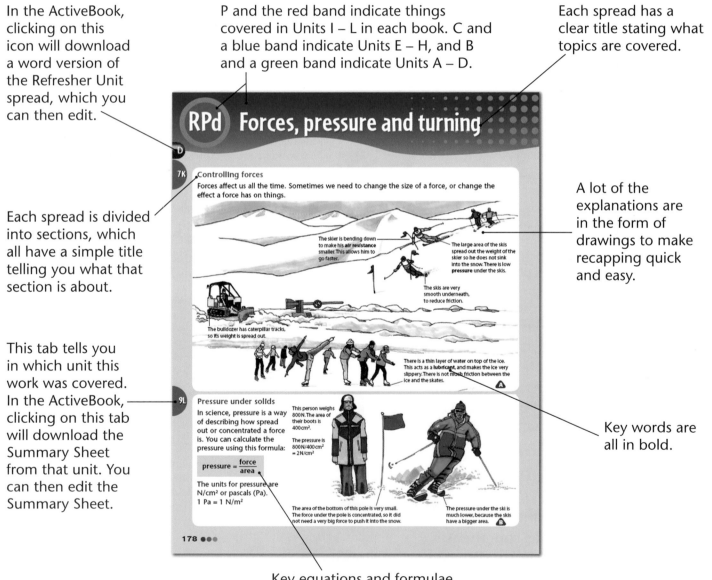

RPd Forces, pressure and turning

7K Controlling forces
Forces affect us all the time. Sometimes we need to change the size of a force, or change the effect a force has on things.

The skier is bending down to make his **air resistance** smaller. This allows him to go faster.

The large area of the skis spread out the weight of the skier so he does not sink into the snow. There is low **pressure** under the skis.

The skis are very smooth underneath, to reduce friction.

The bulldozer has caterpillar tracks, so its weight is spread out.

There is a thin layer of water on top of the ice. This acts as a **lubricant**, and makes the ice very slippery. There is not much friction between the ice and the skates.

9L Pressure under solids
In science, pressure is a way of describing how spread out or concentrated a force is. You can calculate the pressure using this formula:

$$\text{pressure} = \frac{\text{force}}{\text{area}}$$

The units for pressure are N/cm² or pascals (Pa).
1 Pa = 1 N/m²

This person weighs 800N. The area of their boots is 400cm².

The pressure is 800N/400cm² = 2N/cm²

The area of the bottom of this pole is very small. The force under the pole is concentrated, so it did not need a very big force to push it into the snow.

The pressure under the ski is much lower, because the skis have a bigger area.

178 ●●●

7A Skeletal systems

Organ systems are made of different **organs** working together. Organs are made of **tissues**. Each tissue is made of the same type of **cells**. The skeletal systems of plants and animals are organ systems (bones are living organs).

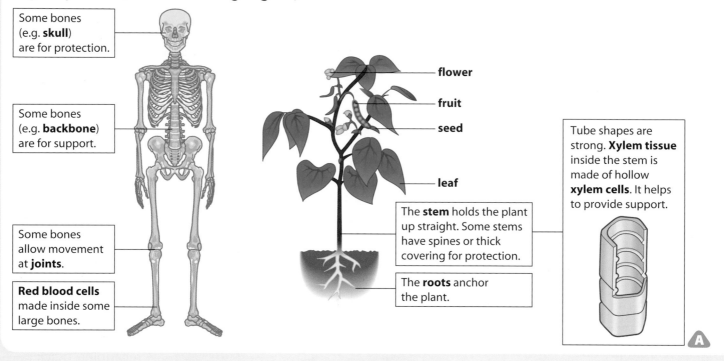

Some bones (e.g. **skull**) are for protection.

Some bones (e.g. **backbone**) are for support.

Some bones allow movement at **joints**.

Red blood cells made inside some large bones.

flower

fruit

seed

leaf

The **stem** holds the plant up straight. Some stems have spines or thick covering for protection.

The **roots** anchor the plant.

Tube shapes are strong. **Xylem tissue** inside the stem is made of hollow **xylem cells**. It helps to provide support.

A

9B Movement

Plants move (e.g. by spreading their seeds) to reach new areas. Animals move to escape predators or find food. Animals use **muscles** to move. A **vertebrate** skeleton has **joints** in which bones are moved by muscles. The skeleton together with the muscles is called the locomotor system.

Exercise strengthens muscles and bones but sports may cause injuries (e.g. 'pulled muscles'). Injuries can make moving difficult, as can diseases (e.g. arthritis) and **deficiency diseases** (e.g. a lack of calcium in the diet can cause **rickets**).

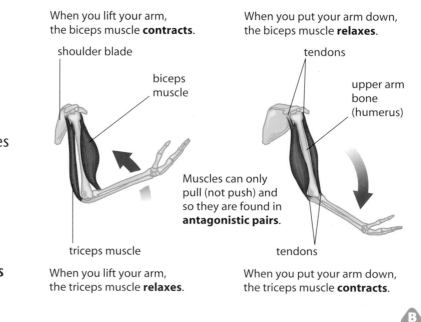

When you lift your arm, the biceps muscle **contracts**.

shoulder blade

biceps muscle

When you put your arm down, the biceps muscle **relaxes**.

tendons

upper arm bone (humerus)

Muscles can only pull (not push) and so they are found in **antagonistic pairs**.

triceps muscle

When you lift your arm, the triceps muscle **relaxes**.

tendons

When you put your arm down, the triceps muscle **contracts**.

B

Animal sensitivity

Like movement, sensitivity is a life process. Many animals have obvious **sense organs** (e.g. eyes). When light strikes the **retina** at the back of your eye, electric **impulses** are sent to the brain to allow you to see. When sound waves reach the **cochlea** in the ear, impulses are sent to the brain to allow you to hear.

Your **nervous system** allows you to **respond** to the **stimuli** that your sense organs detect. Sometimes the response is a **hormone** being released into your blood (e.g. adrenalin is released if you see something scary). Responses to stimuli help organisms to survive.

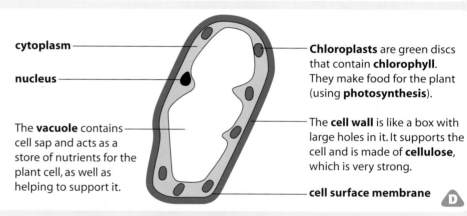

ear
eye
nose
tongue contains taste buds that detect chemicals
skin

brain

Electrical impulses are sent from sense organs along **neurons** to your **brain**. Your brain then sends impulses to other parts of your body to make you react.

The **spinal cord** is a large collection of nerves (many neurons bundled together).

Neurons are **adapted** to their function by being very long and having many connections.

The **cell surface membrane** is like a very thin bag. It keeps the cell together and controls what enters and what leaves.

The **cytoplasm** is like a watery jelly. Most of the cell's activities occur here.

The **nucleus** controls the cell.

C

Plant sensitivity

Plants, like animals, can detect and respond to **environmental factors**, such as light and temperature. For instance, plants always grow towards the light to help them get enough light for photosynthesis. **Chloroplasts** detect light.

cytoplasm

nucleus

The **vacuole** contains cell sap and acts as a store of nutrients for the plant cell, as well as helping to support it.

Chloroplasts are green discs that contain **chlorophyll**. They make food for the plant (using **photosynthesis**).

The **cell wall** is like a box with large holes in it. It supports the cell and is made of **cellulose**, which is very strong.

cell surface membrane **D**

Internal factors

As well as detecting changes around them, animals and plants also detect changes occuring inside them. **White blood cells** are found in your blood, and some detect **microbes** that enter your body. They then help to destroy them, often by creating **antibodies**. An **immunisation** causes white blood cells to create antibodies against a particular disease so that you don't get it.

Microbes that cause diseases include **bacteria** (e.g. TB), **viruses** (e.g. measles) and **fungi** (e.g. athlete's foot).

Some internal factors can cause problems for your senses. Some diseases can cause neurons to stop working. Other problems affect sense organs (e.g. cataracts).

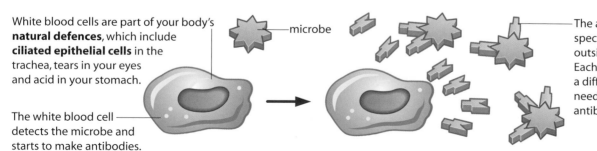

White blood cells are part of your body's **natural defences**, which include **ciliated epithelial cells** in the trachea, tears in your eyes and acid in your stomach.

microbe

The antibodies are made specially to fit onto the outside of the microbe. Each type of microbe has a different surface and so needs a different type of antibody.

The white blood cell detects the microbe and starts to make antibodies.

E

7B Animal lifecycles

A number of factors can affect lifecycles. For instance, **diet** affects human reproduction. A lack of **vitamin** B9 in a pregnant woman's diet increases the risk that her child will suffer from a disease called spina bifida. Other lifestyle choices can also have effects. For example, carbon monoxide gas in cigarette smoke can lead to **premature** babies.

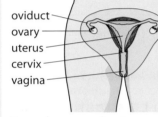
Female reproductive system.

oviduct
ovary
uterus
cervix
vagina

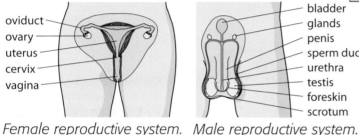
Male reproductive system.

bladder
glands
penis
sperm duct
urethra
testis
foreskin
scrotum

Fertilisation occurs in an oviduct forming a **fertilised egg cell**. This divides and forms an **embryo**. During the **gestation period** the embryo **implants** itself in the lining of the **uterus** and grows into a **foetus**. The **placenta** gets food and oxygen from the mother's blood. These are taken to the foetus via the **umbilical cord**. The foetus is protected by amniotic fluid, held in the **amnion** (**amniotic sac**).

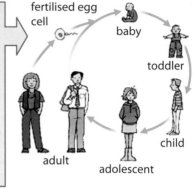

fertilised egg cell
baby
toddler
child
adolescent
adult

During **puberty**:
pubic and underarm hair grows, body smell gets stronger.
Girls: develop breasts and ovaries start to release egg cells.
Boys: voices break, hair grows on face and chest, and testes start to produce sperm cells.

A *Human lifecycle.*

9C / 9D Plant lifecycles

Weeds are plant **pests**. They **compete** with crop plants and reduce their **yield**. The **pesticides** used to control them are called **weedkillers** or **herbicides**. Diagram B shows the lifecycle of a common weed that can spread quickly.

Insects carry **pollen** from the **anthers** of one flower to the stigma of another. This is **pollination**.

The dandelion 'flower' is actually many flowers. A **pollen tube** grows down the style of each flower and into the **ovule** where it **fertilises** an **egg cell**.

pollen grain
stigma
pollen tube
style
ovary
ovule
egg cell

The **seedling** grows into a plant, which then has **flowers**.

The fruits carry the seeds to new areas. This is seed dispersal.

ovary turns into a **fruit**

ovule turns into a **seed**

The seed starts to grow – it **germinates**.

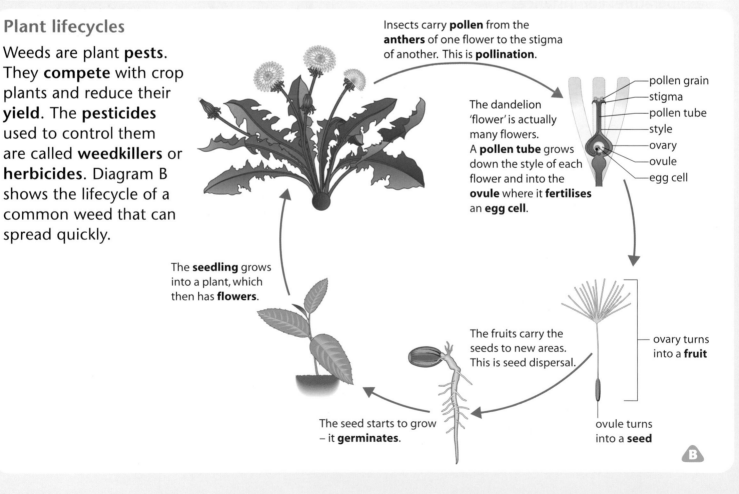

B

Sexual and asexual reproduction

In **sexual reproduction** the **chromosomes** from two organisms (one male and one female) are mixed together, and so the **offspring** have **characteristics** from both **parents**. Sexual reproduction causes genetic variation.

In **asexual reproduction**, part of a parent plant grows into a new plant, creating a **clone**. Asexual reproduction is faster than sexual reproduction but, since there is no genetic variation, one disease would kill all the plants.

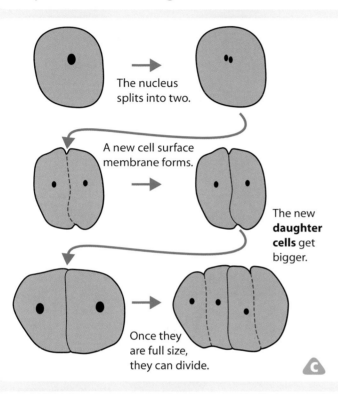

The nucleus splits into two.

A new cell surface membrane forms.

The new **daughter cells** get bigger.

Once they are full size, they can divide.

C

Growth

When organisms grow, their cells increase in number by **cell division**.

The growth of our bodies is controlled by chemical **hormones** in the blood.

The growth of animals is affected by their **genes** and environmental factors (e.g. diet). A person may have genes that cause tallness, but the person will only become tall if they eat a good diet.

The **digestive system** works to break down food, which is then carried in the **circulatory system** to cells that need it. Glucose from food is used for **aerobic respiration**. Oxygen for this process is taken from the air by the **breathing (respiratory) system**. Respiration provides energy for growth.

Specialised cells

The genes in the nucleus of a cell control what the cell does, how big it grows and how fast it grows. The genes in the cells of tissues and organs control how big they can grow.

A fertilised egg cell divides quickly and so do the cells in a embryo, so that the embryo develops quickly making it more likely to survive.

Many cells become specialised – **adapted** to certain **functions** and unable divide any more. For example, red blood cells (which carry oxygen) cannot divide or increase in size and need to be replaced (in humans about once every 120 days). Poisons can stop a cell performing its function (e.g. carbon monoxide stops red blood cells from carrying oxygen).

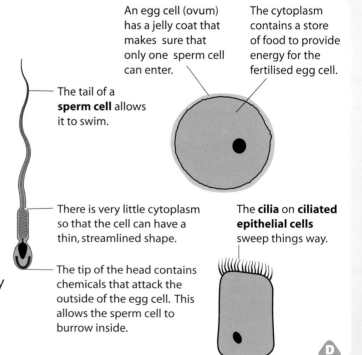

An egg cell (ovum) has a jelly coat that makes sure that only one sperm cell can enter.

The cytoplasm contains a store of food to provide energy for the fertilised egg cell.

The tail of a **sperm cell** allows it to swim.

There is very little cytoplasm so that the cell can have a thin, streamlined shape.

The tip of the head contains chemicals that attack the outside of the egg cell. This allows the sperm cell to burrow inside.

The **cilia** on **ciliated epithelial cells** sweep things way.

D

8B Respiration

Plant and animal cells release energy mainly by **aerobic respiration**:

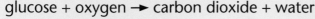

glucose + oxygen → carbon dioxide + water

The oxygen and glucose is transported to cells in the **circulatory system**, which is made up of the **heart** and **blood vessels** (**arteries, veins** and **capillaries**). Plants can transport glucose in **phloem vessels**.

The oxygen is taken into our bodies using the **breathing (respiratory) system**. The lungs are full of air sacs, made of alveoli, which give them a large surface area to absorb oxygen. Plants can take in oxygen through the **stomata** their leaves. Leaves are often wide and flat to give them a large surface area.

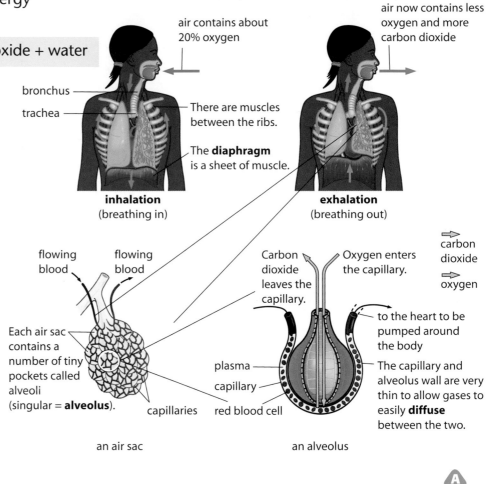

air contains about 20% oxygen

air now contains less oxygen and more carbon dioxide

bronchus

trachea

There are muscles between the ribs.

The **diaphragm** is a sheet of muscle.

inhalation (breathing in)

exhalation (breathing out)

flowing blood

flowing blood

Each air sac contains a number of tiny pockets called alveoli (singular = **alveolus**).

capillaries

an air sac

Carbon dioxide leaves the capillary.

Oxygen enters the capillary.

carbon dioxide

oxygen

plasma

capillary

red blood cell

to the heart to be pumped around the body

The capillary and alveolus wall are very thin to allow gases to easily **diffuse** between the two.

an alveolus

A

8B Excretion

The carbon dioxide from respiration needs to be **excreted** (got rid of) by the lungs because it can stop cells working. The movement of gases into and out of the blood in the lungs is called **gas exchange**. Lung diseases can reduce the surface area for gas exchange and so cause shortness of breath (e.g. TB, which is caused by a **bacterium** and emphysema, which can be caused by smoking.

The kidneys are also **excretory organs**. They remove poisons (created by reactions inside cells) from your blood. The skin can also be an excretory organ, removing some waste materials in your sweat. You sweat to cool you down.

Some **micro-organisms (microbes)** excrete useful products. For example, yeasts produce alcohol (used in brewing) and carbon dioxide (which is used to make bread rise). Other microbes produce **antibiotics**.

8C

Nutrition

All animals, including humans, need a **balanced diet** to stay healthy: the right amounts of **carbohydrates** (for energy), **proteins** (for growth and repair), **fats** (for energy storage) and a good supply of **vitamins** and **minerals** (for health). Lack of vitamins and minerals can cause **deficiency diseases** like scurvy.

Active people need more carbohydrates than less active people. People who are still growing or have very physical jobs also need lots of protein.

Carbohydrates, proteins and fats usually need **digesting** in the **digestive systems**. This means that they are broken down into small pieces so that they can be **absorbed** into the blood.

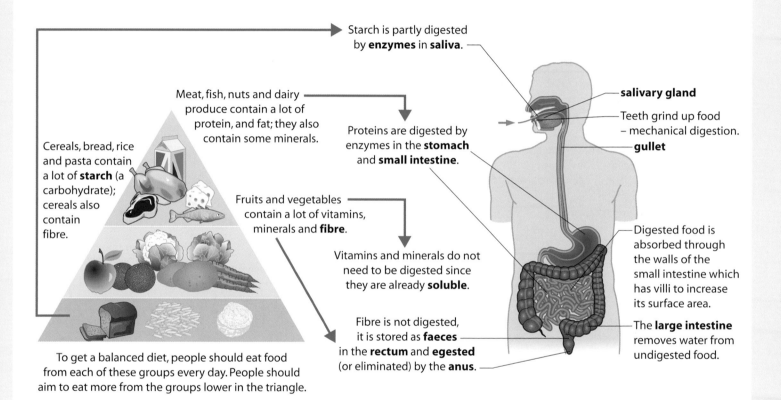

Starch is partly digested by **enzymes** in **saliva**.

Meat, fish, nuts and dairy produce contain a lot of protein, and fat; they also contain some minerals.

Cereals, bread, rice and pasta contain a lot of **starch** (a carbohydrate); cereals also contain fibre.

Fruits and vegetables contain a lot of vitamins, minerals and **fibre**.

Proteins are digested by enzymes in the **stomach** and **small intestine**.

Vitamins and minerals do not need to be digested since they are already **soluble**.

Fibre is not digested, it is stored as **faeces** in the **rectum** and **egested** (or eliminated) by the **anus**.

salivary gland

Teeth grind up food – mechanical digestion.

gullet

Digested food is absorbed through the walls of the small intestine which has villi to increase its surface area.

The **large intestine** removes water from undigested food.

To get a balanced diet, people should eat food from each of these groups every day. People should aim to eat more from the groups lower in the triangle.

B

Plant nutrition

Plants use **photosynthesis** to produce glucose, which they then use to turn into a whole variety of different substances:

carbon dioxide + water → glucose + oxygen

Plants get the carbon dioxide they need from the air (and from their own respiration). The water they need is taken in through their roots, using specialised **root hair cells**. Plants turn the glucose produced into a whole variety of different substances (e.g. starch for storage, cellulose for cell walls).

A root hair cell has an extension to give it more surface area to get water out of the ground quickly.

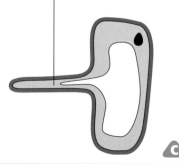

C

7D Classification

Organisms are **classified** as different species by the **variations** in their **characteristics**. A species is a set of organisms that can breed to produce organisms that can also breed. For instance, penguins and owls are two different **species**.

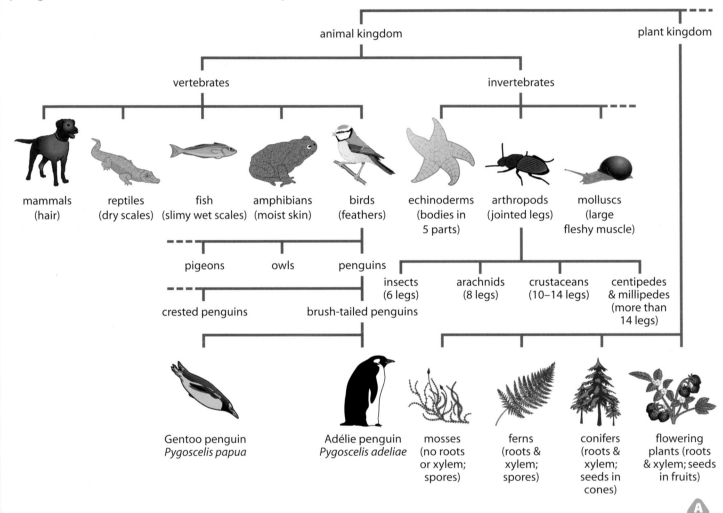

A

9A Variation

Members of the same species have similar characteristics but also show variation. **Environmental variation** is caused by **physical environmental factors** while genetic variation is caused by genes.

People can cause variation in plants and animals. **Selective breeding** is when a characteristic is selected and only organisms with the best examples of the characteristic are used to breed. This can be used to create new **varieties** of plants or new **breeds** of animals.

Scientists can also use **genetic modification** (**genetic engineering**) to put genes from one species into another.

Adaptations

Organisms are **adapted** to their **habitats** so that they can survive. Penguins have woolly feathers under their outer feathers, which trap heat and keep them warm. They also have a thick layer of fat – a very good heat insulator.

Conditions change during the course of a day (**daily changes**) and the course of a year (**seasonal changes**). Many organisms are adapted to these changes. For example, some flowers only open during the day to avoid wasting scent at night (when their pollinating insects are not active).

Animals also have adaptations for finding food … and avoiding being eaten.

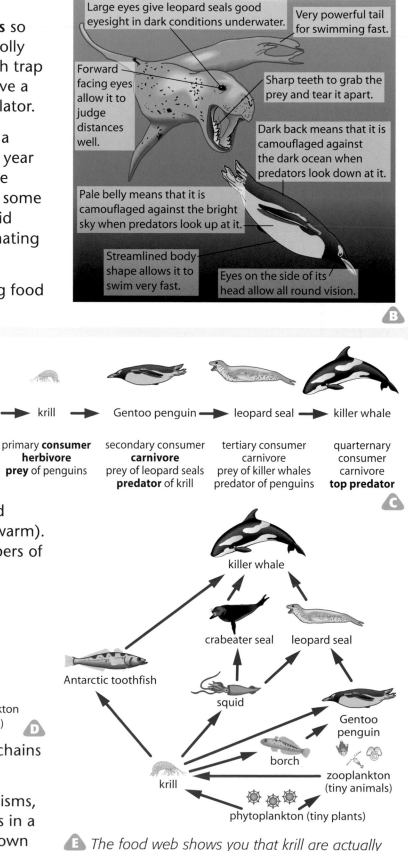

Large eyes give leopard seals good eyesight in dark conditions underwater.

Very powerful tail for swimming fast.

Forward facing eyes allow it to judge distances well.

Sharp teeth to grab the prey and tear it apart.

Dark back means that it is camouflaged against the dark ocean when predators look down at it.

Pale belly means that it is camouflaged against the bright sky when predators look up at it.

Streamlined body shape allows it to swim very fast.

Eyes on the side of its head allow all round vision.

B

Feeding relationships

Food chains show how energy is transferred from organism to organism. All food chains must start with plants because they can trap energy from the Sun.

phytoplankton (tiny plants) → krill → Gentoo penguin → leopard seal → killer whale

| **producer** | primary **consumer** **herbivore** **prey** of penguins | secondary consumer **carnivore** prey of leopard seals **predator** of krill | tertiary consumer carnivore prey of killer whales predator of penguins | quarternary consumer carnivore **top predator** |

C

Energy is lost by each organism in a food chain (e.g. by using it to move or keep warm). A **pyramid of numbers** shows the numbers of organisms in a food chain.

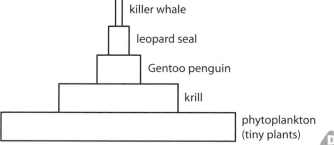

killer whale

leopard seal

Gentoo penguin

krill

phytoplankton (tiny plants)

D

A **food web** shows how the many food chains in a habitat fit together.

Poisons and diseases can kill some organisms, meaning that there is less food for others in a food web. Some poisons do not break down and are passed along food chains.

killer whale

crabeater seal   leopard seal

Antarctic toothfish

squid

Gentoo penguin

borch

zooplankton (tiny animals)

krill

phytoplankton (tiny plants)

E *The food web shows you that krill are actually **omnivores**.*

9D Internal and external stimuli

A **behaviour** is a **response** (reaction) to something happening – the **stimulus**. Stimuli can be internal (inside the organism) or external (outside of it). For example, light is an external stimulus.

Internal stimuli include things like body temperature and substances in the blood. When your body temperature falls (the stimulus), you start to shiver. This causes movement of muscles (the response), which produces heat to warm you up.

The pupils of your eyes control how much light enters. In bright light the pupils are small so that less light enters. Too much light could damage the sensitive **retina** at the back of the eye. In dim light the pupils are large.

Adult blowflies only fly around when it is light.

The **larvae** of blowflies move away from light because their food is found in dark places.

Some plants move their leaves to face the Sun as it appears to move across the sky. This is so that they can get the most light possible for **photosynthesis**. **A**

9D Innate and learned behaviours

Behaviours change as organisms grow up. Some behaviours are automatic. These are **innate behaviours**. Other behaviours are **learned behaviours**.

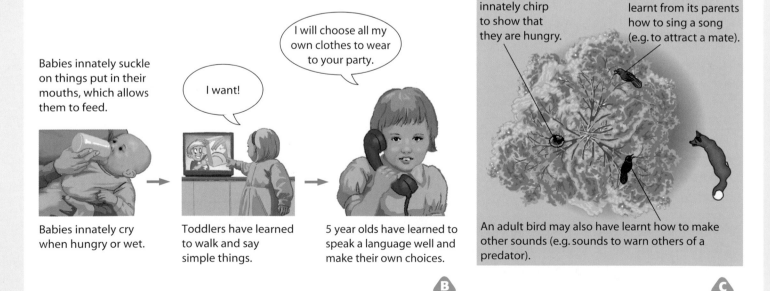

Babies innately suckle on things put in their mouths, which allows them to feed.

I want!

I will choose all my own clothes to wear to your party.

Babies innately cry when hungry or wet.

Toddlers have learned to walk and say simple things.

5 year olds have learned to speak a language well and make their own choices.

Young birds innately chirp to show that they are hungry.

An adult bird has learnt from its parents how to sing a song (e.g. to attract a mate).

An adult bird may also have learnt how to make other sounds (e.g. sounds to warn others of a predator).

B

C

Environmental changes

Changes in the environment of an organism act as external stimuli, and organisms will change their behaviours as conditions change.

Behaviours like migration affect the **populations** of animals in an area.

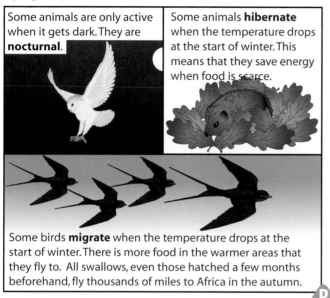

Some animals are only active when it gets dark. They are **nocturnal**.

Some animals **hibernate** when the temperature drops at the start of winter. This means that they save energy when food is scarce.

Some birds **migrate** when the temperature drops at the start of winter. There is more food in the warmer areas that they fly to. All swallows, even those hatched a few months beforehand, fly thousands of miles to Africa in the autumn. **D**

Social behaviour

A behaviour in which an animal communicates with or responds to another animal of the same species is called **social behaviour**. Adults teaching their offspring is a good example of social behaviour. Other examples are shown in drawing E.

Bees do a waggle dance to show other bees where to find food.

Many male animals fight to 'win' females. This makes sure that the strongest animals pass on their genes.

Lions in a pride have a hierachy – each lion knows his/her place. This makes sure that animals don't fight and so damage or kill each other. **E**

Drugs and behaviour

As people grow up, they sometimes experiment with **drugs**. Drugs can be dangerous and affect your behaviour. Governments want to stop people using dangerous drugs.

Scientists carry out a lot of research on drugs but their opinions can be biased. It is important for scientists to publish their results and for other scientists to check the findings. For example, in 2002 Dr. George A. Ricaurte published a paper in a scientific journal showing evidence that ecstasy caused permanent brain damage very quickly in monkeys. However, other scientists questioned the results. Later, it was found that he had used a different drug, and not ecstasy, in his experiments.

Some scientists accuse Dr Ricaurte of publishing incorrect data in order to get more money from anti-drugs groups and governments.

When looking at scientific evidence, scientists used **criteria** to decide if the evidence is good:
* is the evidence valid? (Is it relevant to the question asked?)
* is it accurate? (Were the measurements as accurate as possible?)
* is it reliable? (Can the results be repeated?)

Tobacco contains an addictive chemical called **nicotine**, which makes the arteries narrower. Tobacco smoke also contains carbon monoxide and tar, which damage the **circulatory** and **breathing** (**resiratory**) systems.

Depressants slow the speed with which impulses travel through the nervous system.

heroin

ecstasy

caffeine

The **side-effects** of alcohol can include vomiting.

Stimulants increase the speed with which impulses travel through the nervous system.

These are all **recreational drugs** but these last two are illegal. **F**

7G

The particle model

In science we use **models** to help make ideas easier to understand. For example, we can explain some of the properties of matter if we imagine that it is made up of small round **particles** that behave a bit like marbles. This particle model uses something we know and understand well (i.e. marbles) to explain how tiny invisible particles might behave.

States of matter

The three **states of matter** have different properties due to the arrangement of their particles. For example, the particles in a solid are held by **bonds** in a regular framework very close to each other. They only vibrate about fixed points. So solids have fixed shapes and volumes and do not flow. Sugar can flow but it is **classified** as a solid because each little grain has the properties of a solid. When liquid water **evaporates** it turns into a gas (**steam**). The hotter the water, the faster this **reversible** change will happen.

The particles in a **gas** look like this:

The particles in a **solid** look like this:

The particles in a **liquid** look like this:

A

8E

Dissolving

When a solid **dissolves** in a liquid, the particles of solid split up and mix in with the particles of liquid to make a **solution**. A solid that can dissolve in a liquid is described as **soluble**.

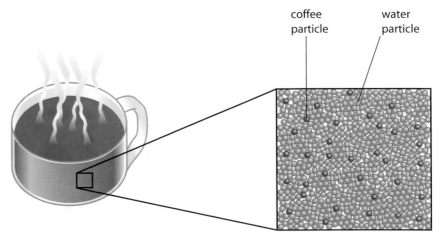

coffee particle

water particle

B

Filtration

Insoluble solids can be separated from a liquid using a process called **filtration** (or **filtering**). Diagram C shows how pure sugar is made from sugar cane by separating the sugar from the other **insoluble** substances in the plant.

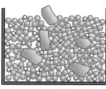
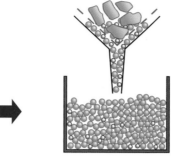

The cane is chopped into small pieces, and mixed with the **solvent** (water, shown in blue). The sugar (white) dissolves in the water, but the rest of the stem (green) is insoluble.

The mixture is then **filtered**. The sugar solution passes through the filter, because both water particles and dissolved sugar particles can fit through the tiny holes in the filter paper. The insoluble solids are trapped.

The solution is then heated so that most of the water evaporates. As the hot syrup cools down, sugar **crystals** form.

C

Distillation

Distillation can be used to separate a solvent from a solution. The solution is heated and the solvent evaporates. The vapour rises and **condenses** as it cools down, turning back into a liquid. In this way, the liquid solvent can be separated from the solution.

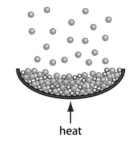

liebig condenser

solution

distilled solvent

heat

D

Diffusion

We can use the particle model to explain **diffusion**; substances spread out and mix together even if we do not stir them up because particles in liquids and gases are always moving.

Particles in a gas are moving all the time and bump randomly into each other.

The smell will spread in all directions, and some of those particles will be detected by the man's nose. This type of spreading is called diffusion.

Perfume particles evaporate from the skin of the woman.

E

Dyes, indicators and chromatography

Some coloured dyes, such as litmus, change colour when they are mixed with acids or alkalis. They are used as **indicators** and can be used to work out the **pH** of a liquid. Mixtures of coloured dyes can be separated by **chromatography**.

Water particles travel up the paper. They carry the particles of the dyes with them.

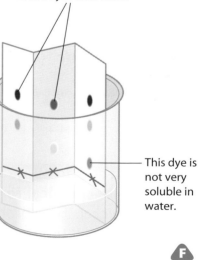

This dye is not very soluble in water.

F

RCb Chemical reactions

8G Elements, mixtures and compounds

Air is a **mixture** of several gases. Some of these gases are **elements** and some are **compounds**.

Oxygen is an element. A **molecule** of oxygen contains two identical **atoms**.

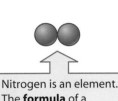

Carbon dioxide is a compound made of two elements. A molecule of carbon dioxide contains three atoms.

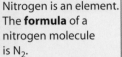

Nitrogen is an element. The **formula** of a nitrogen molecule is N_2.

Water is another compound. The formula of a water molecule is H_2O. In the air, water can be in the form of a gas (water vapour), or drops of liquid water (clouds). **A**

9E / 9F Reactions with metals

Metal objects react with chemicals in the environment around them.

Illustrations **B**, **D** and **E** show **chemical reactions**. The metal elements change colour because they are turning into new substances: chemical compounds. The reactions are **irreversible**.

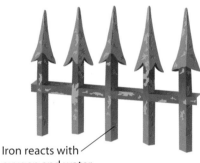

Iron reacts with oxygen and water to form rust. **B**

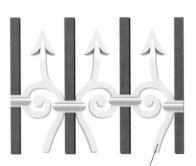

Painting iron railings stops the oxygen and water getting to the metal. **C**

The compounds can be cleaned off the metals by scraping (a physical method). Alternatively acids can be used (a chemical method). For instance, silver polish containing acids can be used to remove the unwanted silver compounds from the surface of the trophy in **D**. Metal oxides (e.g. silver oxide) are bases. Bases **neutralise** acids to make salts:

Black silver oxide tarnish. **D**

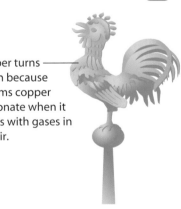

Copper turns green because it forms copper carbonate when it reacts with gases in the air. **E**

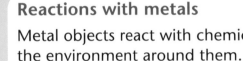

acid + base → salt + water

8G Alloys

Stainless steel is an **alloy**: a mixture of different metals. Unlike compounds, mixtures do not have definite **chemical formulae**. Stainless steel often contains about 70% iron, 20% chromium and 10% nickel. The chromium forms a thin, invisible layer of a compound called chromium oxide (Cr_2O_3) on the surface. This protects the metal from attack and stops it rusting, making it especially useful for appliances such as taps.

Atoms and equations

We can use the particle model to show what happens when a metal reacts with oxygen to form a metal oxide.

Each oxygen atom in an oxygen **molecule** reacts with a magnesium atom. This produces two 'lots' of magnesium oxide.

The atoms have been rearranged, but the total number of atoms is the same at the end as it was at the start.

We can write this as a **symbol equation**.

$$2Mg + O_2 \rightarrow 2MgO$$

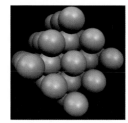 + 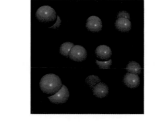 →

Atoms in solid magnesium are all the same and are packed in a regular pattern.

Oxygen gas contains molecules that are spread out. Each molecule is made of two identical atoms, which are bonded strongly together.

Magnesium oxide is a solid compound. There are two different types of atoms, with equal numbers of each, so the formula is MgO.

F

Metals and the periodic table

The **periodic table** groups all the elements we know about according to their properties.

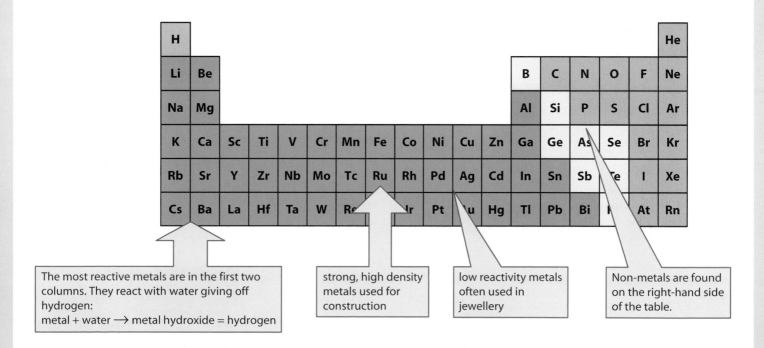

H																	He
Li	Be											B	C	N	O	F	Ne
Na	Mg											Al	Si	P	S	Cl	Ar
K	Ca	Sc	Ti	V	Cr	Mn	Fe	Co	Ni	Cu	Zn	Ga	Ge	As	Se	Br	Kr
Rb	Sr	Y	Zr	Nb	Mo	Tc	Ru	Rh	Pd	Ag	Cd	In	Sn	Sb	Te	I	Xe
Cs	Ba	La	Hf	Ta	W	Re	Ir	Pt	Au	Hg	Tl	Pb	Bi		At	Rn

The most reactive metals are in the first two columns. They react with water giving off hydrogen:
metal + water → metal hydroxide = hydrogen

strong, high density metals used for construction

low reactivity metals often used in jewellery

Non-metals are found on the right-hand side of the table.

G

7F What is a fuel?

A **fuel** is a substance that burns when it reacts with oxygen: this is **combustion**. When fuels are burnt, the atoms in the fuel join with oxygen atoms to make oxides, and energy is released. This energy can then be transferred, for example to heat water in our homes, as kinetic energy in a car engine, or to a turbine to generate electricity in a power station.

Petrol burns in the car engine to produce the energy to move the car along (**kinetic energy**).

Only about 30% of the energy from the fuel is transformed into kinetic energy. The rest is wasted as heat and sound.

A

7F Burning fossil fuels

7I

Fossil fuels are coal, oil and natural gas. They are found under the ground and have taken millions of years to form. They are **non-renewable**, because it takes much longer to produce the fuel than it does to use it.

Natural gas is mostly methane, which is made of carbon and hydrogen.

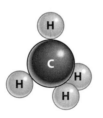

Methane reacts with the oxygen in the air.

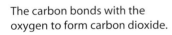

The carbon bonds with the oxygen to form carbon dioxide.

The hydrogen bonds with the oxygen to form water.

B

Biofuels

Biofuels are obtained from plants. The plants store energy that originally came from the Sun, and this energy is released when a biofuel is burned. Biofuels are **renewable** energy resources because new crops can be planted to replace the fuel that is burned.

Wood is a renewable fuel that has been used for hundreds of years.

Some plants have oily seeds. The oil can be extracted and used as a fuel (biodiesel).

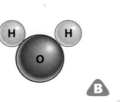

Plants that contain carbohydrates can be fermented to make alcohol, which can be mixed with petrol.

C

Burning hydrogen

Hydrogen is a fuel that burns in oxygen to give water as the only product. It could be used to replace petrol as a fuel for cars.

*Electricity can be used to **D** split up compounds into elements, in a process called **electrolysis**. Here, for example, hydrogen is produced when an electric current is passed through water.*

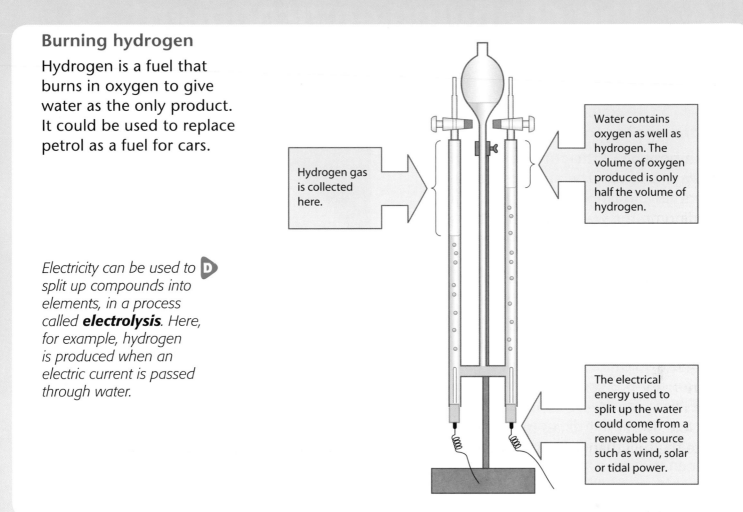

Hydrogen gas is collected here.

Water contains oxygen as well as hydrogen. The volume of oxygen produced is only half the volume of hydrogen.

The electrical energy used to split up the water could come from a renewable source such as wind, solar or tidal power.

Burning metals

Many metals can also be used as fuels because they release energy (heat) when they are combined with oxygen in the air.

metal + oxygen → metal oxide

The amount of energy produced depends on the metal's postion in the **reactivity series**. For instance, metals lower in the reactivity series (e.g. copper) may react with oxygen without burning. Metals even lower in the series (e.g. gold) do not react at all. They thus produce little energy and are ineffective fuels. On the other hand, more reactive metals (e.g. magnesium) burn more violently to form oxides and produce a lot more energy.

However, not even reactive metals are commonly used as fuels. This is because they first need to be extracted from their **ores** by electrolysis and the electrical energy needed to do this is greater than the heat you would get back by burning them.

E *Magnesium (a reactive metal) gives off large amounts of energy when it combines with oxygen in the air.*

9G The atmosphere today

The composition of the atmosphere on Earth is shown in chart **A**. The atmosphere also contains varying amounts of water vapour, depending on the weather. Remember that **NOW** the main gases in the air are **n**itrogen, **o**xygen and **w**ater vapour.

9G The atmosphere in the past

In the past, the atmosphere was very different. A source of evidence is the gas that comes from volcanoes. Most of the gas from the volcano in **B** is water vapour and carbon dioxide, with smaller amounts of other gases such as sulphur dioxide, ammonia, nitrogen and methane. These gases would have been the same millions of years ago, and would have collected in the atmosphere. Although we will never know for sure, our best estimate is that the atmosphere on Earth before life developed was mostly these gases.

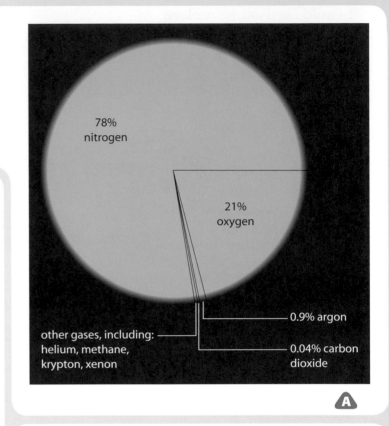

78% nitrogen

21% oxygen

0.9% argon

other gases, including: helium, methane, krypton, xenon

0.04% carbon dioxide

A

B

Why did the atmosphere change?

When the first algae evolved, about 3 800 million years ago, they used **photosynthesis** to turn carbon dioxide and water into glucose and oxygen. The level of carbon dioxide in the air started to drop and the amount of oxygen rose. The oxygen in our atmosphere today has all been produced by alga and plants. If we find oxygen in the atmosphere of another planet, this would be very strong evidence that there was life on that planet.

Now, human activity could be changing the atmosphere. The burning of fossil fuels releases carbon dioxide into the atmosphere. Clearing forests by burning not only adds carbon dioxide to the air but also removes trees that could have used carbon dioxide and produced oxygen.

Carbon dioxide levels

Carbon dioxide is released into the air by **combustion** of fuels and by **respiration** in plants and animals. It is removed from the air by **photosynthesis** and by **dissolving** in the oceans. If these processes are totally balanced, the amount of carbon dioxide in the air would always stay the same.

However, the amounts of gases in the atmosphere are changing. The **carbon cycle** shows the processes that take carbon dioxide out of the atmosphere and those that release it.

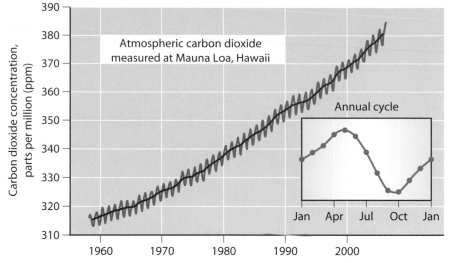

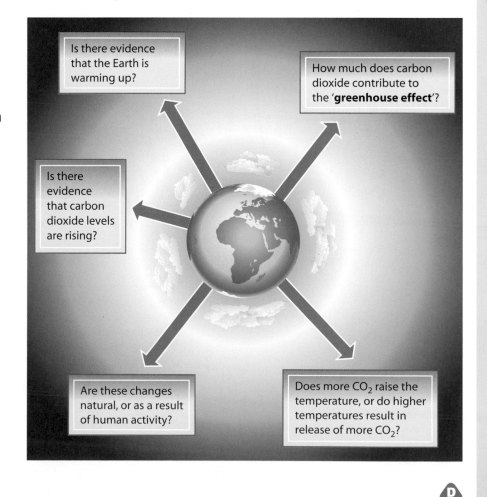

C *Levels of carbon dioxide change on a daily, monthly and yearly basis. Carbon dioxide levels fall during the summer when there is more photosynthesis. The trend over the last 50 years has been for an increase in carbon dioxide levels.*

The greenhouse effect and global warming

The debate about **global warming** is one of the most important of our age. The most widely accepted theory is that global warming is being caused by increasing amounts of carbon dioxide in the atmosphere. Some scientists argue that there is not enough evidence yet. Others have been accused of bias in the way that they interpret the evidence, for example if they work for an oil company or an environmental campaign group.

Scientists may not yet be sure of all the answers, but they will keep questioning and checking the evidence until we are sure they have a theory that fits the facts. Some of the key questions are shown in **D**.

D

8H The rock cycle

The **rock cycle** is a model that can be used to understand the formation of different rocks.

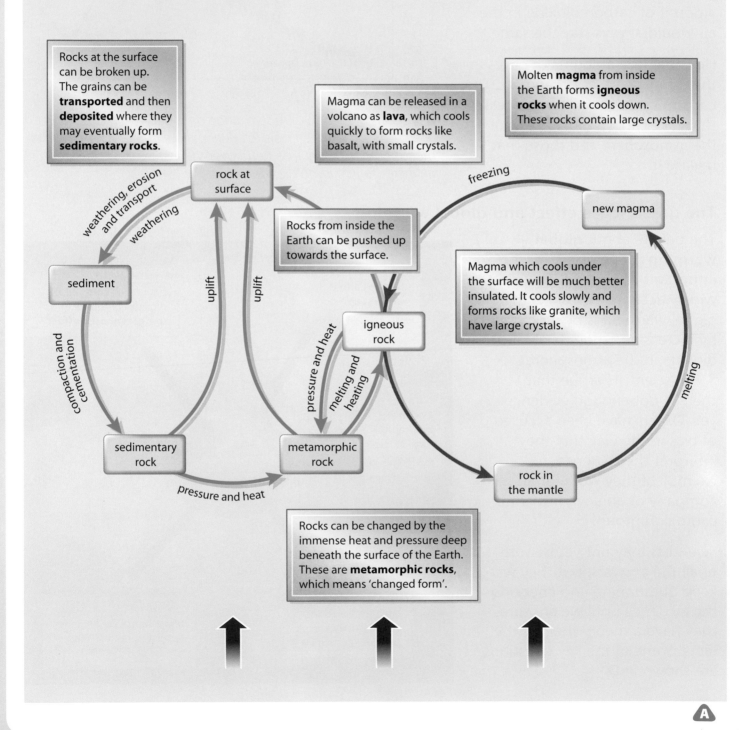

Rocks at the surface can be broken up. The grains can be **transported** and then **deposited** where they may eventually form **sedimentary rocks**.

Magma can be released in a volcano as **lava**, which cools quickly to form rocks like basalt, with small crystals.

Molten **magma** from inside the Earth forms **igneous rocks** when it cools down. These rocks contain large crystals.

Rocks from inside the Earth can be pushed up towards the surface.

Magma which cools under the surface will be much better insulated. It cools slowly and forms rocks like granite, which have large crystals.

Rocks can be changed by the immense heat and pressure deep beneath the surface of the Earth. These are **metamorphic rocks**, which means 'changed form'.

rock at surface

new magma

sediment

igneous rock

metamorphic rock

sedimentary rock

rock in the mantle

weathering, erosion and transport

weathering

uplift

uplift

compaction and cementation

pressure and heat

pressure and heat

melting and heating

freezing

melting

A

Rocks for building

Rocks are used for building materials. The type of rock used will depend on the properties and the availability of materials locally.

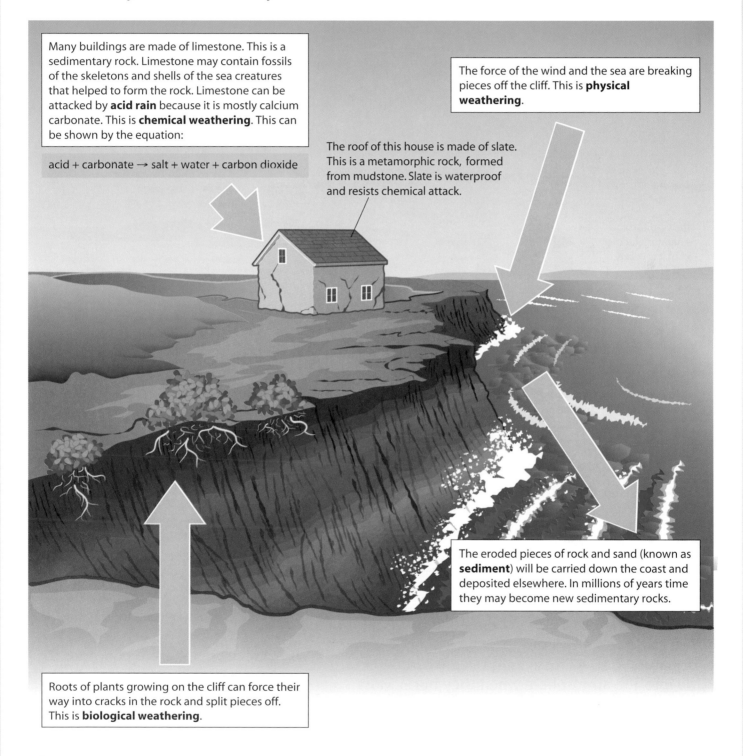

Many buildings are made of limestone. This is a sedimentary rock. Limestone may contain fossils of the skeletons and shells of the sea creatures that helped to form the rock. Limestone can be attacked by **acid rain** because it is mostly calcium carbonate. This is **chemical weathering**. This can be shown by the equation:

acid + carbonate → salt + water + carbon dioxide

The roof of this house is made of slate. This is a metamorphic rock, formed from mudstone. Slate is waterproof and resists chemical attack.

The force of the wind and the sea are breaking pieces off the cliff. This is **physical weathering**.

The eroded pieces of rock and sand (known as **sediment**) will be carried down the coast and deposited elsewhere. In millions of years time they may become new sedimentary rocks.

Roots of plants growing on the cliff can force their way into cracks in the rock and split pieces off. This is **biological weathering**.

B *The house is in danger of disappearing into the sea, as the cliff is being **eroded**. Science cannot answer questions about whether the house is worth saving. The government, the local council and residents will have to decide whether they can afford to stop the erosion taking place and whether it is worth it.*

Energy resources

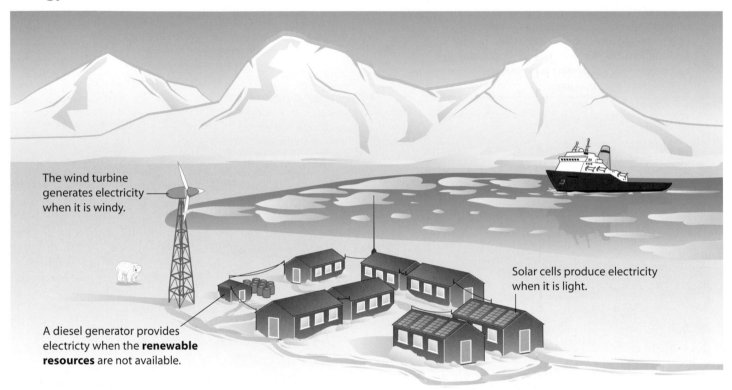

The wind turbine generates electricity when it is windy.

A diesel generator provides electricty when the **renewable resources** are not available.

Solar cells produce electricity when it is light.

A

7I

On the Arctic island of Spitsbergen, there are a group of scientific research stations. In a research station several different **energy resources** are used to generate electricity.

Diesel is made from crude oil, which is a **fossil fuel**. Coal, oil and natural gas are also fossil fuels. Most electricity that people use is generated in power stations. Power stations burn fossil fuels such as coal or natural gas. All fossil fuels release carbon dioxide into the atmosphere when they burn. Most scientists now agree that carbon dioxide added to the atmosphere is causing **global warming**.

We must try to reduce the amount of fossil fuels we put into the atmosphere. One way this can be done is to use renewable resources such as **hydroelectricity**, tides or waves to generate electricity.

Collaboration

Scientists from many different countries work together in research stations. This **collaboration** allows:

- scientists to work in larger teams to develop more accurate ways of measuring things
- scientists from different countries to share knowledge and discuss ideas
- scientists with different interests (e.g. birds, the weather) to work together
- scientists to pool their data so that they have more data, which provides more reliable **evidence**
- the different countries to share the costs of running the station.

Energy transfers

When we use energy resources we **transfer** the energy stored in them to other places or other forms of energy. The generator transfers chemical energy stored in the diesel fuel to electricity. The electricity transfers the energy to appliances such as fridges, lights and computers. Some of the **chemical energy** is also transferred to wasted heat energy.

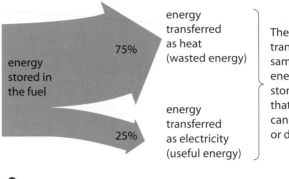

energy stored in the fuel

75% energy transferred as heat (wasted energy)

25% energy transferred as electricity (useful energy)

The total energy transferred is the same as the energy that was stored in the fuel that burnt. Energy cannot be created or destroyed.

B *Sankey diagram* for a generator. Its **efficiency** is 25%.

Electricity

Electricity is a way of transferring energy, not an energy resource. The lights in the buildings are all on one **parallel circuit**. If they were on a **series circuit** the lights would get dimmer as more were switched on. If one light in a series circuit broke, all the others would go off.

If one light breaks it does not affect the others.

electricity supply from generator

Each light can be switched on and off separately.

The fuse is for safety. If there is a fault and the current increases, the wire inside the fuse heats up and melts. This breaks the circuit.

C *Lights in buildings are part of a parallel circuit.*

The cells are **in series** to give a bigger voltage. This will make a bigger current flow, so the bulb will be brighter. The current can also be changed by changing the **resistance** of components in the circuit.

The current is the same everywhere in the circuit.

The bulb transfers useful light energy (and wasted heat energy) to the surroundings.

Energy is stored in the cells. It is transferred to electrical energy when the switch is pressed.

D *The torch uses a series circuit.*

Energy and food chains

Animals need energy to stay alive. The energy stored in food originally came from the Sun. This Sankey diagram shows how energy is transferred between the organisms in a habitat.

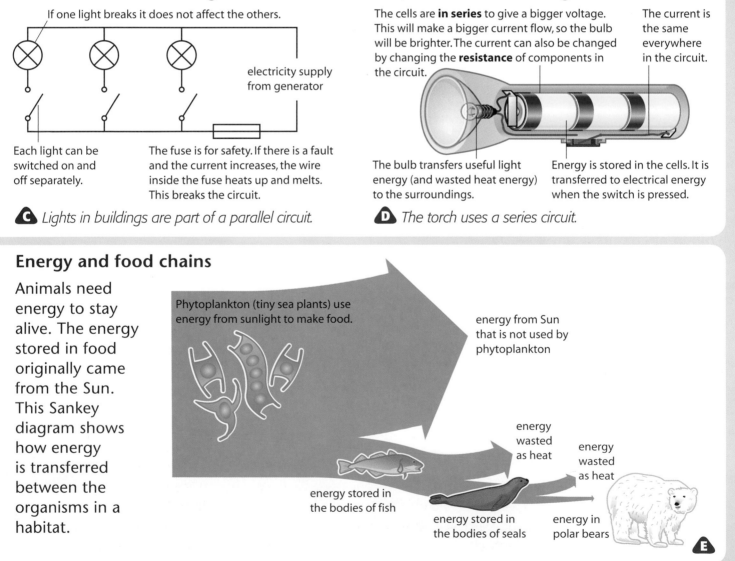

Phytoplankton (tiny sea plants) use energy from sunlight to make food.

energy from Sun that is not used by phytoplankton

energy wasted as heat

energy wasted as heat

energy stored in the bodies of fish

energy stored in the bodies of seals

energy in polar bears

E

91

Transferring energy

The people at this rock concert are detecting energy transferred by light and sound. They keep warm because their clothes reduce the amount of energy transferred away from their bodies by heat.

Light travels in straight lines. White light is a mixture of different colours that our eyes see as white.

Energy is transferred to the spotlights by electricity. The spotlights transfer this energy to light and heat energy.

The loudspeakers transfer electrical energy to sound energy.

The people are wearing clothes to reduce the amount of heat energy transferred by their bodies. The clothes are heat insulators.

A

8K

Coloured lights

You can split up white light into the different colours using a **prism**. This is called **dispersion**. Coloured light can also be made using **filters**.

Some lights have coloured **filters** in front of them. The filters only let one colour in white light through. They **absorb** the other colours.

The white top looks red, and the blue trousers look black.

White materials **reflect** all the colours in light.

Red materials reflect red light and absorb the other colours.

Black materials absorb all the colours in white light.

B

Transferring heat

Energy can be stored in the form of heat. The higher the temperature of an object, the more heat energy it stores. An object with more mass can store more heat energy than an object with a smaller mass.

Heat is transferred from warmer materials to cooler ones. We can use the particle model of matter to help us to think about some of the ways in which heat is transferred.

Heat from the spotlight warms the air near it. The particles move faster and the air becomes less dense. The air rises, and forms a **convection current**.

Convection happens in liquids and gases.

Heat is transferred through solids by **conduction**. Heat energy makes the particles vibrate. The vibrations are passed on because the particles are close to each other.

Heat can also be transferred by **infrared radiation**. Infrared radiation is similar to light.

The spotlight is hotter than the materials around it, so it transfers heat to its surroundings.

C

Sound waves

Light can travel through empty space, but **sound waves** need a **medium** to travel through. Sound can travel through solids, liquids or gases. It travels fastest through solids, because the particles in solids are closer together and can pass the vibrations along quickly.

The slinky is a **model** that can help us to think about how sound energy is transferred.

We hear sounds when the vibrations in the air make parts of our ears vibrate.

Sounds that are too loud can damage our ears.

The loudspeaker vibrates to produce sound. The vibrations are passed on by air **particles**.

Sound waves can be represented on an oscilloscope.

The **amplitude** is the height of a wave. Loud sounds are transferred by waves with large amplitudes.

One wave

The number of waves passing each second is the **frequency**, and is measured in **hertz (Hz)**. High-pitched sounds have high frequencies.

High frequency sounds have shorter **wavelengths**.

D

7K Forces around us

Forces act on everything around us. Forces can change the shape of things and the **speed** at which they move. Forces are measured in **newtons (N)**.

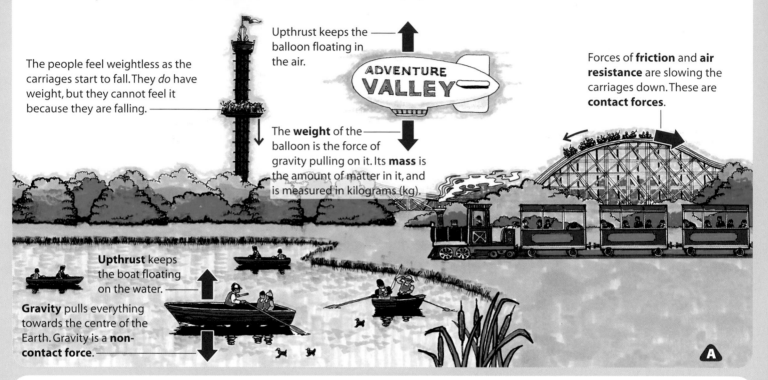

The people feel weightless as the carriages start to fall. They *do* have weight, but they cannot feel it because they are falling.

Upthrust keeps the balloon floating in the air.

Forces of **friction** and **air resistance** are slowing the carriages down. These are **contact forces**.

The **weight** of the balloon is the force of gravity pulling on it. Its **mass** is the amount of matter in it, and is measured in kilograms (kg).

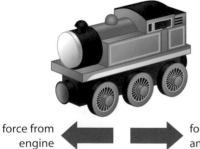

Upthrust keeps the boat floating on the water.

Gravity pulls everything towards the centre of the Earth. Gravity is a **non-contact force**.

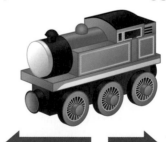

A

9K Balanced and unbalanced forces

We can use arrows to show the sizes of forces. The longer the arrow, the bigger the force.

The **speed** of the train measures how far it travels in a certain time.

force from engine ⟷ force from friction and air resistance

The train is moving at a constant speed because the forward and backwards forces on it are **balanced**.

force from engine ⟷ force from friction and air resistance

The train is accelerating because the forwards force is bigger than the backwards force. The forces are **unbalanced**.

B

The units for speed are in metres per second, miles per hour or kilometres per hour. The speed is worked out using this formula:

$$\text{speed} = \frac{\text{distance}}{\text{time}}$$

Magnets

Magnetism is a non-contact force and is often used in the world around us. For example, modern roller coaster rides use magnets to slow the carriages down at the end of the ride.

A bar magnet is a **permanent magnet**. Magnets can attract things made out of **magnetic materials** (**iron**, **cobalt** or **nickel**).

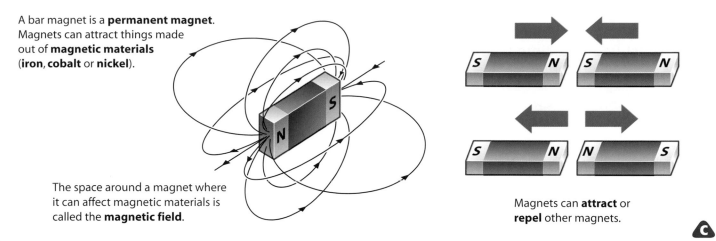

The space around a magnet where it can affect magnetic materials is called the **magnetic field**.

Magnets can **attract** or **repel** other magnets.

C

Electromagnets

Magnets can also be made using electricity. An **electromagnet** is a magnet made using an electric current.

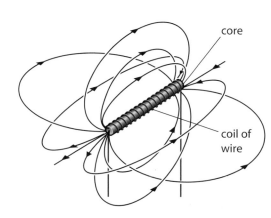

An **electromagnet** is a magnet made using an electric current. Its magnetic field is similar to the magnetic field of a bar magnet.

The strength of an electromagnet increases if:
- the current increases
- there are more coils of wire
- the core is made from a magnetic material.

D

Electromagnets can be used for many things, including safety locks that stop the roller coaster carriages moving off until all the passengers are on board.

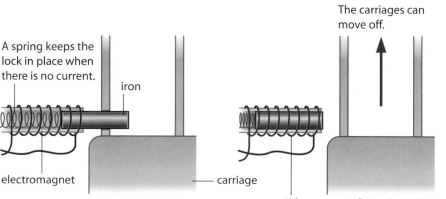

A spring keeps the lock in place when there is no current.

iron

electromagnet

carriage

The carriages can move off.

When current flows through the coil it forms a magnetic field. This attracts the iron.

E An electromagnetic lock.

7K Controlling forces

Forces affect us all the time. Sometimes we need to change the size of a force, or change the effect a force has on things.

The skier is bending down to make his **air resistance** smaller. This allows him to go faster.

The large area of the skis spread out the weight of the skier so he does not sink into the snow. There is low **pressure** under the skis.

The skis are very smooth underneath, to reduce friction.

The bulldozer has caterpillar tracks, so its weight is spread out.

There is a thin layer of water on top of the ice. This acts as a **lubricant**, and makes the ice very slippery. There is not much friction between the ice and the skates.

A

9L Pressure under solids

In science, pressure is a way of describing how spread out or concentrated a force is. You can calculate the pressure using this formula:

$$\text{pressure} = \frac{\text{force}}{\text{area}}$$

The units for pressure are N/cm^2 or pascals (Pa).
$1\,Pa = 1\,N/m^2$

This person weighs 800 N. The area of their boots is 400 cm^2.

The pressure is 800 N/400 cm^2 = 2 N/cm^2

The area of the bottom of this pole is very small. The force under the pole is concentrated, so it did not need a very big force to push it into the snow.

The pressure under the skis is much lower, because the skis have a bigger area. **B**

Pressure in fluids

We can use ideas about particles to help us to understand pressure in fluids.

The holiday resort is on a mountain. The pressure of the air in the resort is less than it is at sea level. This is because there is less air above pressing down.

Particles in the atmosphere are moving in all directions. The force of the particles hitting things causes pressure. The pressure is equal in all directions.

C

When you suck, you make the pressure inside your mouth lower than the pressure outside.

Air pressure from the atmosphere is pushing on the liquid in the glass.

This pressure is greater than the pressure inside your mouth, and it pushes the drink up the straw.

D

Turning forces

The turning effect of a force is called the **moment**. We use this formula to calculate moments:

moment of the force (N m) = force (N) x perpendicular distance from the pivot (m)

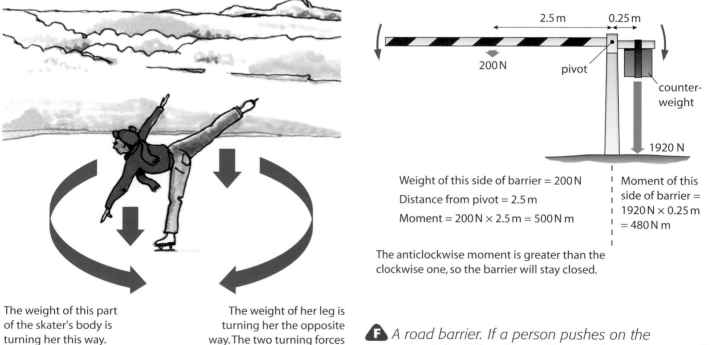

The weight of this part of the skater's body is turning her this way.

The weight of her leg is turning her the opposite way. The two turning forces balance each other.

E

Weight of this side of barrier = 200 N
Distance from pivot = 2.5 m
Moment = 200 N × 2.5 m = 500 N m

Moment of this side of barrier = 1920 N × 0.25 m = 480 N m

The anticlockwise moment is greater than the clockwise one, so the barrier will stay closed.

F *A road barrier. If a person pushes on the counterweight with a force of 20 N, the moments will balance. If the person pushes just a little harder, that side will go down and the barrier will rise.*

7L Earth, Moon and Sun

We can use **models** to help us to explain observations about the Earth, Moon and Sun.

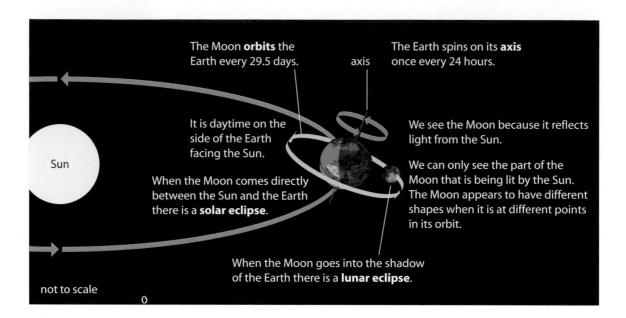

The Moon **orbits** the Earth every 29.5 days.

axis

The Earth spins on its **axis** once every 24 hours.

It is daytime on the side of the Earth facing the Sun.

We see the Moon because it reflects light from the Sun.

When the Moon comes directly between the Sun and the Earth there is a **solar eclipse**.

We can only see the part of the Moon that is being lit by the Sun. The Moon appears to have different shapes when it is at different points in its orbit.

When the Moon goes into the shadow of the Earth there is a **lunar eclipse**.

Sun

not to scale

A *This is the model that astronomers use to explain days, nights and the **phases of the Moon**.*

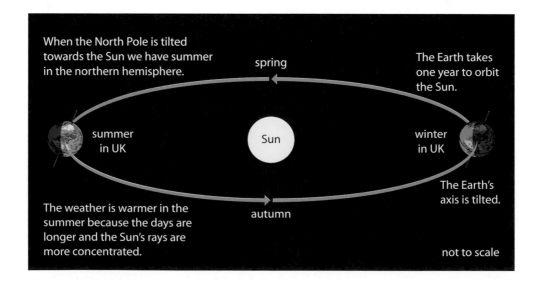

When the North Pole is tilted towards the Sun we have summer in the northern hemisphere.

spring

The Earth takes one year to orbit the Sun.

summer in UK

Sun

winter in UK

The Earth's axis is tilted.

The weather is warmer in the summer because the days are longer and the Sun's rays are more concentrated.

autumn

not to scale

B

The Solar System

The Earth is just one of eight planets that orbit the Sun. The **Solar System** also includes **dwarf planets**, **asteroids** (small lumps of rock), and **comets** (mostly balls of dirty ice). Most of the planets have **moons** (natural satellites) orbiting them.

Working out the models

Most of the early ideas used to explain observations had the Earth in the centre of the **Universe** with the Sun, the Moon and the other planets moving around it. These models were partly based on religious ideas.

These models were used to make predictions about where planets could be observed in the future. Most of the predictions were not very accurate, showing that the models were not very good. Other models were suggested as astronomers from many countries gathered more data, and eventually our current model was accepted.

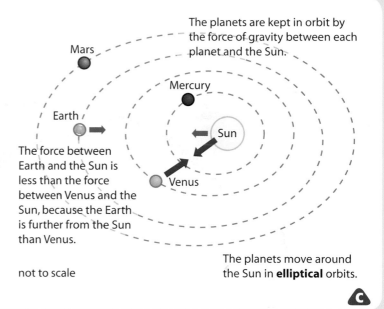

The planets are kept in orbit by the force of gravity between each planet and the Sun.

The force between Earth and the Sun is less than the force between Venus and the Sun, because the Earth is further from the Sun than Venus.

not to scale

The planets move around the Sun in **elliptical** orbits.

C

Gathering data

Most astronomers use telescopes to help them to gather **evidence** about the Solar System and the stars.

Today, telescopes can be put into **satellites** so they can observe the planets and stars from above the atmosphere. Astronomers are also trying to find out about planets orbiting other stars, but we may never know exactly what they are like or if they have life.

Spacecraft called **probes** can be sent to other planets to gather data about them. One day people may be able to visit Mars to explore it. However, it will take a lot of work and money to design and build spacecraft that can carry people safely to other planets.

The telescope uses lenses to help to focus the light.

starlight

to eye

Light changes direction as it goes from one transparent material to another. This is called **refraction**. Refraction happens because light travels faster in air than it does in glass.

D

Glossary

absorb	To take in, for example when water passes from the soil into a root.
accelerate (ack-**sell**-er-ate)	Change speed.
acid rain	Rain which is more acidic (lower pH) than natural rainfall due to the presence of polluting gases such as sulphur dioxide.
adapted	When something has certain features to do a particular function.
addictive	If something makes you feel that you need to have it, it is said to be addictive.
aerobic respiration (air-**O**-bic ress-per-**ay**-shun)	Process that uses up oxygen to release energy from food. Carbon dioxide is produced as a waste gas.
aerodynamicist (air-o-dye-**nam**-i-sist)	A person who studies aerodynamics, which is concerned with the way air flows around vehicles, buildings or other objects.
air quality	How clean or polluted the air is.
air resistance	A force that tries to slow down things that are moving through the air. It is a type of friction.
alkali	A base that dissolves in water.
allele (al-**eel**)	Different variations of the same gene are called alleles.
alloy	A mixture of metals, or of a metal and carbon.
alveoli	Pockets in the lungs where oxygen comes out of the air and goes into the blood. Carbon dioxide is also transferred from the blood to the air in alveoli. Plural = **alveolus**.
amino acid (am-**een**-O ass-id)	The building blocks of proteins.
ammeter	A piece of equipment that measures how much electricity is flowing around a circuit.
amnion	Bag containing amniotic fluid.
amniotic fluid	Liquid surrounding the growing embryo and protecting it.
amp (A)	The unit for measuring current.
amplitude	Half the height of a wave.
anaemia	Deficiency disease caused by a lack of iron. Causes tiredness and shortness of breath.
anorexia	Disease in which someone eats too little and becomes dangerously thin.
antagonistic pair (ant-tag-on-**iss**-tick)	Two muscles that work a joint by pulling in opposite directions, e.g. biceps and triceps.
anther	Part of the male reproductive organ in a flower. It produces pollen grains.
antibiotic	Medicine that can kill bacteria but not viruses.
antibodies	Substances produced by white blood cells that help to fight microbes that might cause diseases.
anus	The opening at the end of the gut.
artery	Blood vessel that carries blood away from the heart.
artificial satellite	A satellite made by humans.
asexual reproduction	Reproduction that only involves one parent. All the offspring are clones of that parent.
asteroid	A small lump of rock orbiting the Sun.
atmospheric pressure (at-mos-**ferr**-ik)	The pressure of the air around us.
atom	The smallest part of an element.
atomic energy	Another name for nuclear energy.
attract	Two things pulling towards each other.
axis	Imaginary vertical line that goes from one pole of the Earth to the other. The Earth spins around its axis.

backbone	The series of small bones that provide the main support for the bodies of humans and other vertebrates.
bacterium	A type of microbe bigger than viruses. Plural = **bacteria**.
balanced diet	Eating a variety of foods to provide all the things the body needs.
balanced forces	When two forces are the same strength, but working in opposite directions.
base	A solid chemical that reacts with an acid to form a salt and water.
behaviour	The way an organism acts or reacts to things around it.
bends	Another name for decompression sickness.
biceps (**bye**-seps)	Muscle at the front of the upper arm that can contract and move the lower arm upwards.
biofuel	A fuel made from plants or from animal droppings.
biological control	Using an organism to keep the numbers of another organism under control. Often a predator.
biological weathering	When rocks are worn away or broken up due to the activities of living things. For example, growing plant roots can split rocks apart.
biomass	The mass of material that an organism makes itself (i.e. not the water it contains or the food it has just eaten). A biomass fuel is a fuel that comes directly from plants, animals or their wastes (e.g. wood, methane from rotting plants).
blood vessel	Tube in which blood flows. There are capillaries, veins and arteries.
bonds	Forces holding particles together.
botanist	A scientist who studies plants.
brain	Organ that controls what the body does.
breathing	Moving muscles to make air flow into and out of the lungs.
breathing system	Made up of the trachea, bronchi and lungs. Gets oxygen into the blood and takes carbon dioxide out of the body.
breed	A group of animals that have different characteristics from other animals of the same species.
breeding	To mate two organisms of the same species to produce offspring.
brittle	Easily broken.
caffeine (**caff**-een)	A stimulant that increases the speed at which nerves carry impulses. Found in coffee, tea and cola drinks.
caisson (**kay**-son)	A box sunk to the bottom of a river and filled with compressed air, to allow people to work on the river bed.
caisson disease (**kay**-son)	The old name for decompression sickness.
calx	A substance like ash from a fire, that was left after a substance burned. Some scientists used to think that all substances were made of a mixture of calx and phlogiston.
cannabis	A drug that can cause memory loss.
capillaries	The smallest blood vessels. Substances enter and leave the blood through the thin walls of capillaries.
carbohydrate	Nutrient that is used as the main source of energy.
carbon cycle	A model showing how carbon is cycled between living organisms and air.
carbon dioxide	A slightly acidic gas formed when carbon reacts with oxygen and during respiration (CO_2).

carnivore	An animal that only eats other animals.
carrier	Someone whose cells contain an allele for a genetic disease is a carrier.
catalytic converter	A device fitted to a car's exhaust to change harmful gases into less harmful gases.
cell (sell)	A source of electricity with a low 'energy' (low voltage). Cells push electrons round a circuit.
cell division	When a cell grows in size and splits in two. Cells increase their numbers using cell division.
cellulose	Insoluble substance made from glucose, which is used to make plant cell walls.
cell surface membrane	Controls what goes in and out of a cell.
cell wall	Tough wall around plant cells. Helps to support the cell.
cemented	Stuck together.
characteristics (kar-ack-ter-riss-ticks)	The features of an organism.
chemical energy	The kind of energy stored in chemicals. Food, fuel and cells (batteries) all store chemical energy.
chemical formula	A combination of symbols and numbers that shows how many atoms of different kinds are in a molecule. In compounds that do not form molecules, it shows the ratio of elements in the compound.
chemical reaction	A reaction in which new substances are made.
chemical weathering	When rocks are broken up or dissolved by chemical reactions, usually involving rainwater.
chlorophyll (klor-O-phil)	Green substance found inside chloroplasts. It traps light energy from the Sun to power photosynthesis.
chloroplast (klor-O-plast)	Green disc containing chlorophyll, found in plant cells. This is where the plant makes food using photosynthesis.
chromatography	Separating dissolved solids from one another. The solids are usually coloured.
chromosome (krO-mO-sOme)	Huge molecule of DNA found inside the nucleus of cells.
cilia	Small hairs on the surface of some cells.
ciliated epithelial cells	Cells in the tubes leading to the lungs that have microscopic hairs, cilia, growing from them.
circulatory system	Organ system containing the heart and blood vessels.
cladding	Thin sheet or layer of metal, stone or other material used to cover walls.
classical conditioning	When a new stimulus causes an innate response previously caused by a different stimulus.
classification	Sorting things into groups.
climate change	The changes that will happen to the weather as global warming happens.
clone	An organism that has identical genes to its parent.
cloning (clO-ning)	The process by which a part of an organism is used to create an identical organism.
cobalt	A metal that is a magnetic material
cocaine (cO-cane)	Very powerful and harmful stimulant that causes blocked arteries and mental problems.
cochlea	A snail shell shaped part of the ear that changes vibrations into electrical impulses.
collaboration	Working together.
combustion	A burning reaction, when a fuel combines with oxygen and releases energy.
comet	A small lump of dirty ice orbiting the Sun.
communications satellite	A satellite used to transmit TV programmes or telephone calls.
compacted	Squeezed by weight above.
compete	When two or more organisms struggle against one another to get the same things, for example food.
component (com-po-nent)	Something in a circuit, like a bulb, switch or motor.

composite material	A material made by combining two or more other materials (the separate materials do not react together).
compounds	Substances that can be split up into simpler substances.
compress	Squeeze together.
compression	Squashing force.
computer model	Using computers to build models involving complex calculations, and using these to make predictions.
concrete (con-creet)	Artificial stone made from a mix of cement, water and larger pieces of material such as gravel, stones or sand.
conduction	The way heat travels through solids.
consumer	An animal that has to eat other organisms to stay alive. Animals are consumers.
contact force	A force that needs to touch an object before it can affect it, for example friction.
contract	When a muscle becomes fatter and shorter.
convection	The transfer of heat in fluids.
corrode	When a substance wears away because it has reacted with a substance such as an acid.
corrosion (cor-roe-shun)	When something (such as stone or metal) reacts with chemicals in the air or water and gets worn away.
counterweights	Weights that help to balance something.
criteria (cry-teer-ee-a)	Set of rules that are used to judge how good or poor something is. Singular = criterion.
cross-breeding	When different varieties or breeds are mated with one another.
crystals	Pieces of a mineral with sharp edges.
current	See electric current.
cystic fibrosis	A genetic disease that causes the lungs and parts of the digestive system to become blocked with sticky fluid.
cytoplasm	Jelly inside a cell where the cell's activities happen.
daily changes	Changes in the physical environmental factors that happen during a day, for example it gets dark at night.
dam	A wall built to hold back water.
decelerate (de-sell-er-ate)	Slow down.
decomposers	Microbes and other smaller organisms that break down dead plants and animals, and animal waste, for example bacteria, fungi and earthworms.
decompression sickness	Bubbles of gas in the blood caused if divers come to the surface too quickly. It can be fatal.
deficiency disease	A disease caused by a lack of a vitamin or mineral.
density	The amount of mass that 1 cm³ of a material has. Denser materials are 'heavier' than less dense ones.
deposit	When moving air, water or ice drops rock fragments or grains (sediment) it has been carrying.
depressant	Drug that decreases the speed at which nerves carry impulses, e.g. alcohol.
diaphragm (dye-a-fram)	Sheet of muscle underneath the lungs. It helps to work the lungs during breathing.
diet	The food that you eat.
diffusion (diff-you-shun)	When particles spread and mix with each other without anything moving them. They move from areas where there are a lot of them to areas where there are fewer of them.
digestion	Process that breaks food into soluble substances in our bodies.
digestive system	The group of organs that carries out digestion.
dispersion	The separating of the colours in light, for example when white light passes through a prism.
displace	When one element takes the place of another in a compound – a type of substitution.
displacement reaction	A reaction where one element takes the place of another in a compound.

dissolving	When a substance splits up and mixes with a liquid to make a solution.
distance multiplier	A machine such as a lever or hydraulic system that increases the distance moved by a force. The force is smaller than the original force.
distance–time graph	A graph that shows how far and how fast something travels during a journey.
distillation	The process of separating a liquid from a solution by evaporating a liquid then condensing it.
DNA	The substance that chromosomes are made from.
dominant allele (al-*eel*)	An allele that has an effect even if other alleles are present.
drag	Air resistance and water resistance are both sometimes called drag.
drug	Substance that affects the way your body works.
ductility	How easily a material is drawn out into a thin wire without breaking.
dwarf planet	A rocky body orbiting the Sun that is not quite big enough to be called a planet, such as Pluto.
Earth observation satellite	A satellite used to take pictures of the Earth – for instance to help forecast the weather.
ecstasy	A stimulant that can cause depression, mental illness and even death.
efficiency (e-*fish*-en-see)	A way of saying how much energy something wastes.
egestion	When faeces are pushed out of the rectum.
egg cell	Female sex cell (gamete).
elastic	Any substance that will return to its original shape and size after it has been stretched or squashed.
elastic potential energy	Another name for strain energy.
electric current	The flow of electrons around a circuit.
electrolysis (ee-leck-*troll*-ee-sis)	A process where electricity is used to split compounds apart, normally to produce an element.
electromagnet	A coil of wire with electricity flowing in it. An electromagnet has a magnetic field like a bar magnet.
electromagnetic spectrum	The family of waves that includes light, infrared, microwaves and radio waves.
electrons	Tiny particles that flow around a circuit.
element	A substance that cannot be split up into anything simpler by chemical reactions. All the atoms in an element are the same.
elliptical (e-*lip*-tick-al)	Oval shaped. The shape of a planet's orbit around the Sun.
embryo (*em*-bree-O)	A ball of cells formed by cell division from a fertilised egg cell.
energy payback time	The time it takes to generate the amount of electricity that was used to make the wind turbine or other generator.
energy resources	Stores of energy that we need for heating, transport and to keep our bodies working.
environmental factors	Things in an environment that can change something about an organism.
environmental variations	Variations in characteristics caused by environmental factors.
enzyme	A chemical that can break up large molecules.
erosion (er-*O*-shun)	The movement of loose and weathered rock.
ethology	The study of animal behaviour.
evaporate	When a liquid turns into a gas.
evidence	Observations, data or measurements that scientists will use to test whether their ideas are correct or not.
excrete	To get rid of waste products from the body.
excretory system	Organ system that removes poisonous substances from your body. It includes the kidneys, liver and bladder.
exhalation	Breathing out.
faeces	Waste food material that is produced by the intestines.

fat	Substance that is used as a store of energy and is important in making cell surface membranes.
fertilisation (fert-ill-eyes-*ay*-shun)	Fusing of a male gamete (sex cell) with a female gamete.
fertilised egg cell	The cell produced when a sperm cell fuses with an egg cell.
fibre	Substance found in food that cannot be used by the body. It helps to keep our intestines clean.
filament	Part of the male reproductive organ in a flower. It supports the anther.
filter	Something which only lets certain colours through and absorbs the rest.
filtering	Separating things that have not dissolved from a liquid. The liquid is passed through a filter to do this.
fitness	If you are able to do all the things that your lifestyle needs you to do, you are fit.
flower	Organ used for reproduction in plants.
flowering plant	Plant with large, flat leaves. Reproduces using seeds found in fruits. Fruits and seeds form inside flowers.
fluid	A liquid or a gas.
foetus	After an embryo has grown all its organs it is called a foetus. This is usually after about 10 weeks.
food chain	A way of showing what eats what in a habitat.
food web	Many food chains linked together.
force	A push or a pull
force-multiplier	A machine such as a lever or hydraulic system that increases the size of a force. The increased force moves through a shorter distance than the original force.
forensic science	Using science to answer legal questions (such as 'who committed a crime?').
formula	See **chemical formula**.
fossil fuels	Coal, oil and natural gas – all fuels that were formed from the remains of dead plants and animals millions of years ago.
frequency	The number of waves each second.
friction	A force that tries to slow things down when two things rub against each other.
fruit	Something used to carry the seeds of flowering plants. Can be fleshy or dry.
fuel	Anything that stores energy that can be converted into heat energy, e.g. fossil fuels and nuclear fuel.
function	Something's job.
fungicide (*fung*-giss-ide)	Pesticide that kills fungi.
fungus	Organisms which are different from animals, plants and bacteria. Examples include mushrooms and yeasts. Plural is **fungi**.
fuse	Join together.
galaxy	Millions of stars grouped together.
galvanising (*gal*-van-ize-ing)	Coating a metal (usually iron or steel) with zinc, to protect it from corrosion.
gamete (*gam*-meet)	Scientific word for sex cell.
gas	Something that does not have a fixed volume or shape and is easy to squash.
gas exchange	Process where oxygen diffuses into the blood and carbon dioxide diffuses out of the blood. It happens in the alveoli in the lungs.
gene (*jeen*)	A section of a chromosome that controls inherited characteristics of an organism.
generate	Make electricity by turning a magnet inside coils of wire.
generator	Large coil of wire with a magnet inside. When the magnet is turned, electricity is produced in the coil of wire.
genetic disease	A disease caused by genes, e.g. cystic fibrosis.
genetic engineering	Adding genes to an organism that are not normally there or removing genes.

genetic information (jen-*et*-tick)	The instructions that control your characteristics. These instructions are found on genes.
genetic modification	A process in which the genes of an organism are altered, often by adding genes from other species.
geology	The arrangement of rocks in the ground.
geostationary orbit	An orbit where a satellite is over the equator and takes exactly 24 hours to circle the Earth, so it always stays over the same part of the Earth.
germination (jerm-in-*ay*-shun)	When a root and shoot start to grow out of a seed.
gestation period	The length of time from fertilisation to birth.
global warming	A theory that says that the Earth is getting hotter because of the activities of humans. It may be caused by too much carbon dioxide in the air.
glucose	Type of sugar made during photosynthesis.
GM	Short for 'genetic modification' or 'genetically modified'.
gravitational potential energy (grav-it-*ay*-shon-al po-*ten*-shall)	The kind of energy stored by anything that can fall down.
gravity	The force of attraction between any two objects.
greenhouse effect	The trapping of the Sun's energy by gases in the atmosphere, which helps to keep the Earth warm.
greenhouse gases	Any gases that contribute to the greenhouse effect. They include carbon dioxide, methane and water vapour.
guard cell	A cell that helps to open and close stomata.
gullet	Organ in the shape of a tube that takes food from your mouth to your stomach.
habitat	The place an organism lives in, for example woodland.
heart	Organ that pumps blood around the body.
heart attack	When the heart muscles start to die because too little blood is getting to them.
heartbeat rate	The number of times the heart beats in one minute.
herbicide (herb-*iss*-ide)	Pesticide that kills plants. Also called a weedkiller.
herbivore	An animal that only eats plants.
heroin	A very dangerous depressant drug. Causes vomiting and severe headaches.
hertz (Hz)	The unit for frequency. One hertz means one wave per second.
hibernation	When animals hide during the winter and go to sleep.
hormone (hor-*moan*)	A chemical messenger produced by some cells in an organism. It travels around the organism and changes what certain cells do.
hybrid (*high*-brid)	An animal that is the offspring of parents from two different species.
hydraulic press	A hydraulic system that increases the force.
hydraulic system (hi-*draw*-lick)	A system that works by transmitting pressure through pipes containing a liquid.
hydrocarbon	A chemical compound containing only hydrogen and carbon.
hydroelectricity (hy-drO-elek-*tris*-it-ee)	Electricity generated by letting falling water (usually from a reservoir) turn turbines and generators.
hydroponics	Growing plants without soil.
ice core	A long cylinder of ice obtained by drilling down into an ice cap. Ice cores can be used to investigate past climates.
igneous rock (*igg*-nee-us)	Rock made from interlocking crystals that are not in layers.
immunisation	Making people immune to diseases.
implantation	When an embryo sinks into the soft lining of the womb.
imprinting	A simple behaviour that is learned during a short 'window' of time in an animal's development.
impulse	An electrical signal carried by neurons.

indicator	A dye that will change colour in acids and alkalis.
in equilibrium (eck-will-*ib*-ree-um)	In balance.
in parallel	One component is in parallel with another when the current divides, a part going through each component, then joins up to complete the circuit.
in series	Components are in series when all the current goes through both of them, one after the other.
insoluble	Something that does not dissolve is said to be insoluble.
infrared radiation	Another name for heat energy that is transferred by radiation. It can travel through transparent things and a vacuum (empty space).
inhalation	Breathing in.
inherited	Passed on to an organism from its parents.
innate behaviour	An automatic, inbuilt behaviour that cannot be changed.
insecticide (in-*sect*-iss-ide)	Pesticide that kills insects.
iron	A metal that is a magnetic material.
irreversible	Permanent change that can't be reversed.
joint	Part of the body where bones are moved by muscles.
Kevlar	A synthetic (manufactured) fibre that is very strong.
kilometres per hour (km/h)	Units for speed when the distance is measured in kilometres and the time is measured in hours.
kinetic energy	The kind of energy stored in moving things.
kwashiorkor (kwash-ee-*or*-kor)	Deficiency disease caused by a lack of protein.
lander	A space probe that lands on a planet or moon.
large intestine	Organ that removes water from unwanted food.
larva	The young of insects, which may look nothing like the adults. Plural = larvae.
lava	Molten rock that runs out of volcanoes.
law of conservation of energy	The idea that energy can never be created or destroyed, only changed from one form of energy to another.
law of conservation of mass	The idea that the total mass of all the reactants in a chemical reaction is the same as the total mass of all the products.
leaf	Plant organ used to make food by photosynthesis.
learned behaviour	A behaviour that has been changed due to the experiences of the animal.
lifecycle	The series of changes in an organism as it gets older.
limiting factor	Something that stops a process from increasing any further.
liquid	Something with a fixed volume but no fixed shape.
lubricant	A substance, normally a liquid, used to reduce friction.
lunar eclipse	When the Moon moves into the shadow of the Earth.
lung cancer	A disease when cells in the lungs start to divide and grow uncontrollably.
m/s/s	Metres per second per second. The units for acceleration, where 1 m/s/s means that the object is increasing its speed by 1 m/s every second.
mains electricity	Current at 230 V provided to houses, shops, etc.
magma	Molten rock beneath the surface of the Earth.
magnetic field	The space around a magnet where it can affect magnetic materials or other magnets.
magnetism	A force that attracts objects made out of iron.
malleability	How easily a material is rolled out into a sheet without breaking.
mass	The amount of matter that something is made of. Mass is measured in grams (g) and kilograms (kg). Your mass does not change if you go into space or to another planet.

mean speed	The total distance something travels divided by the total time taken allows you to calculate its mean or average speed.
medicine (*med-iss-in*)	A drug that helps the body to ease the symptoms of a disease or cure the disease.
medium	Any substance.
metals	Elements that are shiny, conduct heat and electricity well and often have high melting and boiling points.
metamorphic rock (*met-a-mor-fik*)	Rock made from interlocking crystals that are usually lined up or in layers.
metres per second (m/s)	Units for speed when the distance is measured in metres and the time is measured in seconds.
microbe	A very small living thing. Also called a micro-organism.
micro-organisms	A very small living thing.
migration	When animals move to different areas of the world depending on the season.
miles per hour (mph)	Units for speed when the distance is measured in miles and the time is measured in hours.
mineral	Properly called a mineral salt. An element or compound found naturally in rocks. Plants and animals need certain minerals for growth and development.
mineral salt	Chemical found in soil that plants need to grow healthily.
mixture	A substance containing two or more elements that are not chemically joined.
model	A scientific way of thinking about how or why things happen. Allows you to more easily think about how a complicated thing works.
molecule	Two or more atoms joined together.
moment	The turning effect of a force. It is calculated using: moment = force × distance of force from pivot.
monitor	To measure and record data over a period of time.
monomer	A small molecule that can be joined with lots of other ones to make a polymer.
moon	A natural satellite of a planet.
mucus	A sticky fluid produced by your body to trap particles.
muscle cell	Cell that can change its length and so help us to move.
mutation (*mew-tay-shun*)	A change in a gene, which often alters the instructions that the gene carries.
National Grid	System of overhead and underground cables that carry electricity around the country.
natural	Something that occurs in nature. Natural materials include wool from sheep and wood from trees.
natural defences	Your body's way of trying to keep microbes out, for example skin, or killing them if they get inside you, for example stomach acid.
natural gas	Fossil fuel formed from the remains of dead plants and animals that lived in the sea.
natural pollutant	Natural substances that can cause harm to the environment if they are present in high enough concentrations.
natural satellite	A satellite that has not been made by humans. The Moon is a natural satellite of the Earth.
nervous system	The brain, spinal cord and nerves. It uses impulses to communicate with and coordinate the actions of all parts of the body.
neuron	A nerve cell. It carries electrical signals called impulses around the body.
neuron pathway	The route of impulses through a series of neurons in the brain.
neutralisation reaction	A reaction between an acid and a base (or alkali) that makes a solution with a pH of 7. A salt and water are produced.
neutralise	When something is added to an acid or an alkali to make it more neutral – closer to pH 7.
newton (N)	The unit of force.

newton metre (N m)	The unit for the moment of a force.
nickel	A metal that is a magnetic material.
nicotine (*nick-O-teen*)	Poisonous, addictive drug found in cigarettes.
night-blindness	Deficiency disease caused by a lack of vitamin A. You cannot see very well in dim light.
nitrate (*ny-trate*)	Mineral salt needed by plants to make proteins.
nitrogen oxides	Acidic gases formed when nitrogen reacts with oxygen. Includes nitrogen dioxide (NO_2).
nocturnal	Organisms that are active at night.
non-contact force	A force that can affect something from a distance, from example gravity.
non-metal	Elements that are not shiny, and do not conduct heat and electricity well. They often have low melting and boiling points. The solid ones are brittle.
non-renewable	Resource that will eventually run out, such as stone when it is quarried.
nuclear energy	Energy stored inside atoms.
nucleus (*new-clee-us*)	Part of the cell that controls it. Plural = nuclei.
nutrient	A part of your food that is used as a raw material (fat, carbohydrate, protein, vitamins, minerals).
offspring	Any plant or animal formed by reproduction. Offspring are produced by their parents.
omnivore	An animal that eats both plants and other animals.
orbit	The path that a planet takes around a star, or the path that a moon or satellite takes around a planet.
orbiter	A space probe that goes into orbit around a planet or moon.
ore	Rock that contains a metal compound from which the metal can be extracted.
organ	A group of tissues all working together to carry out an important function.
organ system	Collection of organs working together to do an important job.
organic farming	Producing foods without the use of lots of artificial chemicals.
ovary (*O-very*)	Part of the female reproductive organs in a plant. It contains ovules, each of which contains an egg cell.
ovule (*ov-you'll*)	Contains egg cells in plants. Found in the ovary.
ovum (*O-vum*)	Scientific word for a female sex cell. Plural = ova.
oxide (*ocks-eyed*)	A compound formed when something reacts with oxygen.
oxidised (*ocks-ee-dysed*)	When a substance reacts with oxygen to form an oxide.
palisade cell (*pal-is-aid sell*)	Cell found in leaves that contains many chloroplasts.
parallel circuit	A circuit with two or more branches that split apart and join up again.
parent	An organism that has had offspring.
particles	The tiny pieces that everything is made out of.
pascal	A unit of pressure. $1\,Pa = 1\,N/m^2$.
periodic table	A table that shows all the elements, arranged in a regular order to show patterns in properties.
permanent magnet	A magnet that keeps its magnetism, it does not depend on electricity.
persistent	A chemical is persistent if it does not get broken down in nature very quickly. It stays around for a long time.
pest	Any organism that damages a crop.
pesticide (*pest-iss-ide*)	Chemical that kills pests.
pH	A scale which measures how acidic or alkaline a solution is.
phases of the Moon	The different shapes that the Moon seems to have at different times.
phloem vessel (*flow-em*)	Tube made of living phloem cells which transports dissolved substances (e.g. sugars) around a plant.

phlogiston (flo-*jist*-on)	A substance that was thought to be part of most materials. Phlogiston was thought to be given off when things burned.
photosynthesis (fO-tO-*syn*-thes-sis)	Process that plants use to make their own food. It needs light to work. Carbon dioxide and water are the raw materials. Glucose and oxygen are the products.
physical environmental factor	The non-living conditions in the environment of an organism, for example temperature, light.
physical weathering	When rocks are worn away or broken up by physical processes such as changes in temperature.
pivot	A point about which something turns. A pivot is also sometimes called a fulcrum.
placenta	Attached to the uterus wall, this takes oxygen and food out of the mother's blood and puts waste material into the mother's blood.
planet	A large object orbiting a star. The Earth is a planet.
plant hormone (*hor*-moan)	A hormone found in plants.
plastic	A material that keeps its new shape when it has been stretched or squashed.
plating (*play*-ting)	Coating a metal with a thin layer of another metal.
pneumatic tyre (new-*mat*-ick)	A tyre that contains air or gas under pressure.
polar orbit	An orbit where a satellite passes over the North and South Poles. It will pass over all parts of the Earth during several orbits.
pollen grain	The male sex cell in flowering plants.
pollen tube	Tube that grows from a pollen grain down through the stigma and style and into the ovary.
pollination (poll-in-*ay*-shun)	Transfer of pollen from an anther to a stigma.
pollutants	Harmful chemicals present in the environment which are not normally there or only there in harmless concentrations.
pollution	The effects of substances released into the environment in amounts that will cause harm.
polymer	A very long molecule, made from a series of smaller molecules (monomers) joined together.
population	The number of a certain organism found in a certain area.
porous (*por*-us)	Containing tiny holes that water or other liquid can soak into.
potential energy (po-*ten*-shall)	The scientific word for 'stored' energy.
power	The number of joules of energy an appliance transfers every second.
power pack	A source of electricity with a low voltage.
power rating	The label on an appliance that tells us how much energy it transfers.
predator	An animal that catches and eats other animals.
premature	A baby that is born too early and small is said to be premature.
pressure	The force on a certain area, measured in newtons per square metre (N/m^2), newtons per square centimetre (N/cm^2), or pascals (Pa).
prey	An animal that is caught and eaten by another animal.
prism	A block of clear, colourless glass or plastic, which is usually triangular.
probe	See space probe.
proboscis (prob-*oss*-sis)	Tube that many insects use to suck up liquids, which they feed on.
producer	An organism that is able to make its own food. Plants are producers.
product	A new chemical formed in a chemical reaction.
property	Something that is used to describe how a material behaves and what it is like. Strength is a property of some solids.
protein (*pro*-teen)	Chemical that is used for growth and repair.

psychology	The study of human behaviour.
puberty	Time when big physical changes happen in the body of a teenager.
pumped storage	A kind of power station where spare electricity is used to pump water to a high reservoir. This water can be allowed to fall again, to a hydroelectric power station, when electricity is needed.
Punnett square	A model used to work out how likely it is that certain combinations of alleles will be inherited.
pupa	Some insects have larvae that grow and then form a hard case around them (a pupa). The adult form of the insect then hatches out of the pupa.
pyramid of numbers	Way of showing the numbers of different organisms in a food chain.
raw materials	Substances from which other substances are made.
reactants	Chemicals that form new substances during a chemical reaction.
reactive	A substance that reacts with many other substances, or reacts very easily.
reactivity series	A list of metals which shows them in order of their reactivity, with the most reactive at the top.
recessive allele (al-*eel*)	An allele that only has an effect if there are no dominant alleles for a characteristic.
recreational drug (reck-ree-*ay*-shun-al)	Any drug used for its mind-altering effect rather than as a medicine.
rectum	Organ that stores faeces before they are egested.
recycle	Use a material again, often by melting it and using it to make new objects.
red blood cells	Cells in the body that carry oxygen.
reflect	To bounce off something. Light bounces back from a surface instead of passing through it.
refraction	The change in direction when light goes from one transparent material to another.
relax	When a muscle stops contracting and becomes thinner and longer, it relaxes.
renewable resource	An energy resource that will never run out (e.g. solar power).
repel	Push away.
reservoir (*rez*-er-vwar)	The lake formed when a dam blocks a river.
resistance	A way of saying how difficult it is for electricity to flow through something.
resistant	Something that is not affected by disease is said to be resistant to it.
resistor	A component that makes it more difficult for current to flow – resistors are used to control the size of the current in the circuit.
respiration (res-per-*ay*-shun)	Process which occurs in all living cells that releases energy from food. Carbon dioxide is one of the products.
respiratory system	Another name for the breathing system.
response	Reaction to something.
resultant force	The overall force on something, taking into account any forces that balance each other out.
retina	The part inside the eye that converts light into electrical signals. It is the area at the back of the eye that contains receptor cells for light.
re-use	When an object is used again, without being broken up or recycled.
reversible	A change in which what you end up with can easily be turned back into what you started with.
rickets	Deficiency disease caused by a lack of calcium. It causes weak and poorly shaped bones.
rigid	Does not bend easily.
risk assessment	A way of estimating the amount of risk involved in an activity and of taking steps to reduce the risk where necessary.
rock cycle	All the processes which form sedimentary, igneous and metamorphic rocks linked together.
root	Plant organ used to take water out of the soil.

root hair cell	Cell found in roots. It has a large surface area to help the cell absorb water quickly.
rust	Iron oxide – a flaky red compound formed when iron reacts with oxygen.
S factors	Four factors that describe how fit you are: suppleness, strength, stamina and speed.
sacrificial protection	Attaching a more reactive metal to a metal that you wish to protect. The more reactive metal corrodes first – it is sacrificed.
saliva	A digestive juice. It contains an enzyme that breaks down starch into sugar.
salivary gland	Found in the mouth. It makes saliva.
salt	A compound made when acids react with metals or bases. Many salts are chlorides, sulphates or nitrates. Common salt is sodium chloride.
Sankey diagram	A diagram that represents energy transfers by arrows. The width of each arrow depends on the amount of energy it represents.
satellite	Anything that orbits a planet or a moon.
scavenger	An animal that feeds on animals that have already died.
scurvy (skur-vee)	Deficiency disease caused by a lack of vitamin C. The gums bleed and cuts take a long time to heal.
seasonal changes	Changes in the physical environmental factors that happen during the course of a year, for example it gets colder in winter.
sediment	Rock grains and fragments dropped on the bottom of a river, lake or sea.
sedimentary rock	Rock formed from layers of sediment. It is often porous and made of rounded grains.
seed	A part of a plant formed in flowers by sexual reproduction that can grow into a new plant.
seedling	A tiny plant, newly grown from a seed.
selective breeding	When humans choose certain animals and plants that have useful characteristics and breed more of these organisms.
selective herbicide (herb-iss-ide)	Chemical pesticide that kills only some types of plants.
semi-metal	An element that has some metallic and some non-metallic properties.
sense organs	Organs that detect changes in the surroundings of an organism (e.g. eyes, ears, nose, skin).
series circuit	A circuit in which there is only one loop of wire.
sex cell	A cell used for sexual reproduction.
sex chromosomes (krO-mO-sOmes)	Chromosomes that determine the sex of an organism.
sexual reproduction	Producing new organisms by the joining of two sex cells.
side-effect	Harmful or unpleasant effects caused by drugs.
skeleton	All the bones in the body of a vertebrate.
skull	Collection of bones that protect your brain.
small intestine	Organ where most digestion happens. The soluble substances produced by digestion are absorbed into the body here. It is about 6.5 metres long in adults.
social behaviour	How an animal communicates with or reacts to other animals of the same species.
solar eclipse	When the Moon is between the Sun and the Earth, and casts a shadow on part of the Earth.
Solar System	A star with planets and other objects orbiting it.
solid	Something with a fixed volume and shape.
soluble	Something that is soluble can dissolve in a liquid.
solution	When a solid has dissolved in a liquid.
sound waves	Energy carried from one place to another in the form of waves.
solvent	A liquid used to dissolve things.
solvent abuse	Sniffing solvents used in glue and other things.
space probe	An unmanned spacecraft that has cameras and other equipment to find out about other planets.

species (spee-shees)	A group of organisms that can reproduce with each other to produce offspring that will also be able to reproduce.
speed	How fast something is moving. Often measured in metres per second (m/s), miles per hour (mph) or kilometres per hour (km/h).
sperm cell	Male sex cell (gamete).
spinal cord	A large bundle of nerves that runs through the 'backbone' and up into the brain.
stamina	How long your body can exercise for.
star	A huge ball of gas that gives out heat and light energy.
starch	Type of insoluble carbohydrate found in plants and made from glucose. Used as a storage material.
states of matter	There are three different forms that a substance can be in. These are solid, liquid or gas.
steam	Water as a gas. Also called water vapour.
stem	Plant organ used to take water to the leaves and to support the leaves.
stigma	Part of the female reproductive organ in a flower. It is where pollen lands.
stimulant (stim-you-lant)	Drug that increases the speed at which nerves carry messages, e.g. caffeine.
stimulus	A change in the environment of something.
stomach	Organ used to break up food.
stomata (stO-mart-a)	Holes in leaves through which gases diffuse. They are opened and closed by guard cells. Singular = stoma.
strain energy	The kind of energy stored in stretched or squashed things which can change back to their original shapes.
streamlined	Having a smooth shape that reduces the air resistance or water resistance.
strength	How strong your body is.
stroke	When the nerve tissue in the brain starts to die because too little blood is getting to it.
style	Part of the female reproductive organ in a flower. It connects the stigma to the ovary.
sulphur dioxide	An acidic gas formed when sulphur reacts with oxygen (SO_2).
sulphur precipitator (pre-sip-it-ate-or)	A device used in power stations to remove sulphur dioxide gas from the gases coming out of the chimney.
supersonic	Faster than the speed of sound.
suppleness	How easily your body can bend and twist.
sustainable	An action that allows things to continue into the future.
symbol equation	A reaction displayed using the chemical symbols of the substances involved.
synthetic	A material that has been manufactured by humans from raw materials.
tar	A poisonous, black, sticky substance found in cigarette smoke.
tarnish	When a shiny metal gets a dull coating due to the reaction with oxygen.
tension (ten-shun)	Stretching force.
terminal velocity	The maximum speed of an object. Usually only applies to falling objects when the downward force is balanced by drag.
thermal energy	The hotter something is the more thermal energy it has.
tissue	A group of the same cells all working together.
top predator	The last animal in a food chain.
toxic	Poisonous.
transfer	When energy is changed from one form into another or from one place to another we say it is transferred.
transport	The movement of rock grains and fragments by wind or water.

trial and error learning	When animals learn to associate an action with a good or bad event by trial and error.
triceps (try-seps)	Muscle at the back of the upper arm that can contract and move the lower arm downwards.
turbine	A machine that is turned by a moving liquid or gas. Turbines are used to turn generators in power stations.
turning effect	The moment of a force. The way in which a force turns something around a pivot.
umbilical cord	Carries food, oxygen and waste between the placenta and the growing foetus.
unbalanced forces	When two forces working in opposite directions are not the same strength.
universal indicator	A mixture of indicators giving a different colour depending on how weak or strong an acid or alkali is.
Universe	All the galaxies and the space between them.
unreactive (un-ree-yak-tive)	A substance that reacts with few other substances, or reacts very slowly or not at all.
upthrust	A force that pushes things up in liquids and gases.
useful energy	Energy that is transferred in the way we need.
uterus	Organ in females in which a baby develops.
vacuole	Storage space in plant cells.
variation (vair-ee-ay-shun)	The differences between things or organisms.
variety	A species of plant may be divided into different varieties, and each variety has a certain set of characteristics making it different from the other varieties.
vein	Blood vessel that carries blood to the heart.
vein (vane)	In plants, a vein contains phloem and xylem tissue.
ventilation	The movement of air into and out of the lungs.
vertebra	Your 'backbone' is made of many bones called vertebrae.
vertebrate	An animal with a backbone.
virus	The smallest type of microbe. Many people think that they are not living because they do not carry out the seven life processes for themselves.
visible light	The part of the electromagnetic spectrum that we can detect with our eyes.
vitamin	Nutrient needed in small quantities for health, for example vitamin C.
voltage	A way of saying how much energy is transferred by electricity.
voltmeter	A component that measures voltage.
volts (V)	The unit for voltage.
vulcanisation	When rubber is heated with sulphur to make it stiffer and less sticky.
wasted energy	Energy that is not useful.
watts (W)	The unit for measuring power. One watt is one joule per second.
wavelength	The distance between the top of one wave and the top of the next.
weathered	Broken down by chemical or physical changes.
weedkiller	Another name for a herbicide.
weight	The amount of force with which gravity pulls something towards the Earth. It is measured in newtons (N).
white blood cell	A type of blood cell that helps to destroy microbes. They either engulf microbes or make antibodies.
wilting	When a plant droops because it has too little water.
word equation	A reaction displayed in words.
xylem cell	Cells used to form tubes of xylem tissue.
xylem tissue	Found in roots, stems and leaves. Transports water. Made of xylem cells.
xylem vessel	A tissue made of hollow xylem cells joined end to end, which transports water through a plant.

yield (yeeld)	The amount of useful product that is obtained from a crop.
zygote (zy-goat)	Scientific word for 'fertilised egg cell'.

The periodic table

1																	2
H hydrogen																	**He** helium
3 **Li** lithium	4 **Be** beryllium											5 **B** boron	6 **C** carbon	7 **N** nitrogen	8 **O** oxygen	9 **F** fluorine	10 **Ne** neon
11 **Na** sodium	12 **Mg** magnesium											13 **Al** aluminium	14 **Si** silicon	15 **P** phosphorus	16 **S** sulphur	17 **Cl** chlorine	18 **Ar** argon
19 **K** potassium	20 **Ca** calcium	21 **Sc** scandium	22 **Ti** titanium	23 **V** vanadium	24 **Cr** chromium	25 **Mn** manganese	26 **Fe** iron	27 **Co** cobalt	28 **Ni** nickel	29 **Cu** copper	30 **Zn** zinc	31 **Ga** gallium	32 **Ge** germanium	33 **As** arsenic	34 **Se** selenium	35 **Br** bromine	36 **Kr** krypton
37 **Rb** rubidium	38 **Sr** strontium	39 **Y** yttrium	40 **Zr** zirconium	41 **Nb** niobium	42 **Mo** molybdenum	43 **Tc** technetium	44 **Ru** ruthenium	45 **Rh** rhodium	46 **Pd** palladium	47 **Ag** silver	48 **Cd** cadmium	49 **In** indium	50 **Sn** tin	51 **Sb** antimony	52 **Te** tellurium	53 **I** iodine	54 **Xe** xenon
55 **Cs** caesium	56 **Ba** barium	57 **La** lanthanum	72 **Hf** hafnium	73 **Ta** tantalum	74 **W** tungsten	75 **Re** rhenium	76 **Os** osmium	77 **Ir** iridium	78 **Pt** platinum	79 **Au** gold	80 **Hg** mercury	81 **Tl** thallium	82 **Pb** lead	83 **Bi** bismuth	84 **Po** polonium	85 **At** astatine	86 **Rn** radon
87 **Fr** francium	88 **Ra** radium	89 **Ac** actinium	104 **Rf** rutherfordium	105 **Db** dubnium	106 **Sg** seaborgium	107 **Bh** bohrium	108 **Hs** hassium	109 **Mt** meitnerium	110 **Ds** darmstadtium	111 **Rg** roentgenium	112 **Uub** ununbium	113 **Uut** ununtrium	114 **Uuq** ununquadium	115 **Uup** ununpentium	116 **Uuh** ununhexium		118 **Uuo** ununoctium

58 **Ce** cerium	59 **Pr** praseodymium	60 **Nd** neodymium	61 **Pm** promethium	62 **Sm** samarium	63 **Eu** europium	64 **Gd** gadolinium	65 **Tb** terbium	66 **Dy** dysprosium	67 **Ho** holmium	68 **Er** erbium	69 **Tm** thulium	70 **Yb** ytterbium	71 **Lu** lutetium
90 **Th** thorium	91 **Pa** protactinium	92 **U** uranium	93 **Np** neptunium	94 **Pu** plutonium	95 **Am** americium	96 **Cm** curium	97 **Bk** berkelium	98 **Cf** californium	99 **Es** einsteinium	100 **Fm** fermium	101 **Md** mendelevium	102 **No** nobelium	103 **Lr** lawrencium

Key:
- metal
- semi-metal
- non-metal

Index